IVAN SIMON

Senior Physicist
Arthur D. Little, Inc.

INFRARED
RADIATION

Published for
The Commission on College Physics

D. VAN NOSTRAND COMPANY, INC.

Princeton, New Jersey

Toronto   *London*   *New York*

D. VAN NOSTRAND COMPANY, INC.
120 Alexander St., Princeton, New Jersey
(*Principal Office*)
24 West 40 Street, New York 18, New York

D. VAN NOSTRAND COMPANY, LTD.
358, Kensington High Street, London, W.14, England

D. VAN NOSTRAND COMPANY (Canada), LTD.
25 Hollinger Road, Toronto 16, Canada

Published simultaneously in Canada by
D. VAN NOSTRAND COMPANY (Canada), LTD.

Preface

When I was beginning to work in infrared spectroscopy I found two small monographs particularly useful. They were C. Schaeffer and F. Matossi's *Das Ultrarote Spektrum* (J. Springer, Berlin, 1930) and G. B. B. M. Sutherland's *Infra-red and Raman Spectroscopy* (Methuen & Co., Ltd., London, 1947). Since they have both become unavailable and somewhat outdated, I have often wondered what I would read today should I want a concise introduction to the broad subject of infrared radiation.

In this book I have tried to give the reader who wishes to find out what infrared is all about a reasonably complete picture and sufficient background for deeper study. To make it easier to find more information about a special topic, each chapter ends with a list of pertinent references. There is also a bibliography at the end of the book which gives references to a few selected monographs not mentioned in the text.

The exposition follows a historical and descriptive pattern. This may sound a bit old-fashioned or inelegant, but for an introduction to a new subject, it makes sense to me. Besides, it always makes me more humble, amidst our electronic instrumentation and sophisticated theory, to think of men who, by the strength of their thought and genius, helped to bring the knowledge of infrared radiation to the state in which we find it today.

I am indebted to many people for what I have learned and what in turn I have endeavored here to convey to my readers. I wish to express thanks in particular to my friends and colleagues at Arthur D. Little, Inc., with whom I have had the good fortune to associate in many research projects dealing with the infrared. To Dr. E. U. Condon, the first General Editor of the Momentum Book Series, go my thanks for the encouragement he gave me to write the book. Finally, I wish to thank Professor Walter C. Michels, the present General Editor, for the critical reading of the manuscript and for many helpful suggestions.

3

I wish to dedicate this book to my wife, Jarmila, who gave me courage, understanding, and support without which I could never have finished it.

I. S.

Table of Contents

1 Introduction

NATURE OF THE INFRARED RADIATION

Infrared radiation, or simply the *infrared*, as it is often called, has a variety of aspects. The original significance of it as a form of heat radiation is perhaps less prominent today than it was at the time of its discovery. The spectroscopic connotations of infrared were obvious from its discovery (in 1800) by Sir William Herschel, who actually repeated Newton's prism experiment but looked for the heating effect rather than the visual distribution of intensity in the spectrum. It appears that the word "infrared" emerged first in the spectroscopic literature some 75 years later, but it is uncertain who was its originator. Spectroscopy was then for a long time a principal domain of research activity in infrared. In fact, application of infrared (molecular) spectroscopy to chemical problems have proved so successful that at present chemists are probably the greatest users of infrared spectrographs.

The importance of infrared as a vehicle of information by "invisible" rays was also recognized quite early, in particular by the military. Before the end of World War I, infrared signaling and detecting systems using the newly discovered photoconductive cells had been put into field service. During World War II, the research effort was still greater and produced substantial progress in infrared technology. One of the best known developments of this period was the photoelectric image converter, which transformed the infrared image of an object illuminated by a filtered "black" radiation of a searchlight into a visible image on a fluorescent screen.

All along, physicists have made the infrared both a subject of their study and a tool for exploring the constitution of matter. Studies of lattice vibrations in ionic crystals by observing their "residual ray" reflectivity in the far infrared or the determination of energy gaps in semiconductors are typical examples of using the infrared in solid state physics. In turn, better knowledge of the nature of the interaction between radiation and matter has led recently to the development of a new type of infrared source (the laser) radically different from the thermal sources in the sense that it generates monochromatic and coherent radiation. The way the laser was conceived and practically realized required that use be made of both the electromagnetic and the quantum nature of the radiation.

However, we are getting ahead of ourselves in the historical sequence of events. It took quite a long time to recognize infrared first as a form of electromagnetic radiation and to discover its other forms in the sense of quantum mechanics. After Herschel discovered the caloric radiation in the solar spectrum beyond the visible red, it was not clear whether the heat rays and the light were of the same kind. Herschel himself became convinced that he had discovered a new type of radiation. Only after J. D. Forbes (in 1834) showed that heat radiation can be polarized in the same manner as light, and after A. H. L. Fizeau and J. B. L. Foucault (in 1837) actually determined the wavelength of near infrared waves from interference fringes, did the identity of infrared with light become generally accepted. In 1865 J. C. Maxwell predicted theoretically the existence of electromagnetic waves and proposed the identity of these waves with light waves. H. Hertz in 1887 produced electromagnetic waves in the laboratory and confirmed that they propagate with the same velocity as light and have the same polarization properties. Finally, in 1923, E. F. Nichols and J. D. Tear succeeded in generating far-infrared waves of 220-micron wavelength by means of a miniature spark oscillator similar to that used by Hertz, thus showing beyond any doubt that infrared radiation too is of an electromagnetic nature.

From the point of view of classical physics this would have been a crowning accomplishment, but it came too late. Even before the end of the century it was becoming clear that it would never be possible to derive from electromagnetic theory alone a generally valid law of spectral distribution of energy of blackbody radiation. The efforts by W. Wien and Lord Rayleigh to derive the radiation law were only partially successful, and tended to disagree sharply with experimental facts at one or the other end of the spectrum (see Fig. 1-1). Finally, by 1900, M. Planck recognized at what point it was necessary to depart from the classical approach. He found that the proper distribution of energy among the elementary oscillators composing the thermally radiating body can be obtained only if one abandons the concept that energy is continuously divisible.

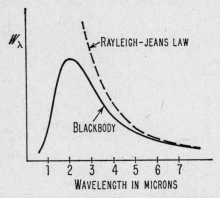

FIG. 1-1 Discrepancy between the observed blackbody emittance curve and that calculated from classical theory.

Planck made this step with some reluctance, since his original approach was based on thermodynamics and electromagnetic theory. The postulate of discontinuous, quantized exchange of radiant energy, which he introduced, appeared to him to be the only alternative leading to a correct theory that would be in agreement with experimental evidence. In fact, immediately after O. Lummer and E. Pringsheim presented the final results of their extensive and accurate measurements of distribution of radiant energy in a blackbody spectrum, Planck published a correct form of the radiation law which he seemed to have derived intuitively, without explicit use of the quantum concept. However, in a following paper which he presented at the December 1900 meeting of the German Physical Society, he restated his theory in a form that contained the specific assumption that the energy states of the elementary oscillators can vary only by integral multiples of elementary quanta $\mathcal{E} = h\nu$. Moreover, Planck found that the energy quanta must be proportional to the frequency ν and determined correctly the magnitude of the proportionality constant h which is now known by his name.

Although this development turned out to have far-reaching consequences, as it led eventually to the development of quantum mechanics, its importance was not immediately obvious. Five years after Planck's discovery, A. Einstein made the first important use of the quantum concept in his theory of the photoelectric effect and established the idea of light quanta as a modern form of Newton's light corpuscles. Later still, in 1913, Bohr introduced his quantum theory of atomic spectra, which in turn led to the founding of quantum mechanics. The concept of light thereupon acquired an aspect of a split personality. Radiation was to be considered at once a wave or a particle, depending on the nature of the interaction with matter. This was, of course, quite abhorrent to Planck's contemporaries, and he made several attempts at reconciling the wave mechanical and the corpuscular views. However, none of his or other attempts succeeded, and physicists had to learn to accept the dual nature of radiation as one of the facts of life.

LAWS OF RADIATION

Electromagnetic Spectrum. Assuming that infrared is a form of electromagnetic radiation, we may "place it on the map" by indicating its domain in the electromagnetic spectrum. This is done in a diagram shown in Fig. 1-2. Here the *wavelength* λ is given in units customary for the various spectral regions, that is, centimeters, microns, and angstroms ($1\mu = 10^{-4}$ cm, $1\text{Å} = 10^{-8}$ cm). As shown in the diagram, infrared extends from about 0.75μ to about 1000μ. The short-wave end borders on the limit of visual perception in deep red, while the long-wave end overlaps with microwave spectrum in the millimeter wave range.

In spectroscopy we often use *wavenumbers* ν' rather than wavelengths. Wavenumber is the number of waves per unit length, or the reciprocal of wavelength. According to established but inconsistent custom, wavenumbers are always given in reciprocal centimeters

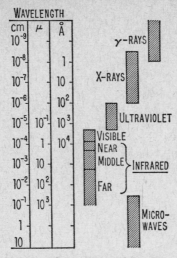

FIG. 1-2 Electromagnetic spectrum.

(cm^{-1}), while wavelengths are given in microns. Thus to a wavelength of 1μ corresponds a wavenumber 10,000 cm^{-1}. In theoretical consideration we prefer to use *frequency* ν (in cycles per second). These quantities are related as follows

$$\lambda = \frac{1}{\nu'} = \frac{c}{\nu}, \tag{1-1}$$

where c denotes the velocity of light, $c = 2.997 \times 10^{10}$ cm/sec. Sometimes confusion may arise from the unfortunate custom of using the same symbol ν for both frequency and wavenumbers.

From the point of view of quantum mechanics, the energy of a quantum of radiation of frequency ν is

$$\mathcal{E} = h\nu, \tag{1-2}$$

where $h = 6.624 \times 10^{-27}$ erg sec is the *Planck constant*. The wavelength associated with a quantum of energy $\mathcal{E}$ is accordingly

$$\lambda = \frac{hc}{\mathcal{E}}. \tag{1-3}$$

Blackbody Radiation. While we recognize the unity of different kinds of radiation in the electromagnetic spectrum, we note that the basic laws of infrared radiation refer to its thermal origin. In particular, these laws are concerned with thermal radiation emitted by various bodies when heated to a certain temperature. We know that such radiation covers a broad *continuum* of wavelengths. Common experience shows that various bodies emit and absorb more or less, depending how "dark" or "bright" their surface coloration appears to be. In order to eliminate this sort of arbitrariness from theoretical considerations, physicists after Kirchhoff postulated a *blackbody* as a most effective radiator and a complete absorber. No single substance (e.g., lampblack or powdered graphite) has this ideal property when examined over a wide spectral range. However, it is found that the radiative characteristics of an aperture in an *isothermal cavity* made of an *opaque*, absorbing material represents almost exactly the property of a blackbody. The process producing the blackbody effect is the multiple traversal of the rays emitted by the walls and reflected from them in a diffuse manner before they reach the aperture and escape into the outer world.

By this process of multiple emission, absorption, reflection, and re-emission, the radiation in the cavity comes to a thermal equilibrium with the walls. The radiation inside the cavity has the same intensity everywhere, and comes and goes in all possible directions in equal strengths; it is homogeneous and isotropic. The intensity of this *blackbody radiation* is a function of temperature only, no matter the kind of material of which the cavity is made. It is also found that the blackbody radiation emerging from the aperture obeys *Lambert's law*, that is, its intensity is greatest in the direction of the normal to the plane of the aperture and decreases with the cosine of the angle between the normal and the direction of observation. Radiation from real bodies seldom approaches this simple law.

For the blackbody the total emissive power or *radiant emittance* is exactly proportional to the fourth power of its absolute temperature (*Stefan-Boltzmann law*). The word total refers here to the entire wavelength spectrum from $\lambda = 0$ to infinity. Emittance is defined as the radiant energy emitted per second per cm^2 of surface area. Energy per second is power; hence emittance may be measured in units of watt cm^{-2}. Temperature T is measured in degrees Kelvin, that is, in Centigrade scale from the absolute zero. If we wish to consider how the emitted radiant energy varies with direction, we define the *radiance* as the power emitted per cm^2 per unit solid angle (steradian).

Emittance W of any real body is less than that of a blackbody. The ratio W/W_b is called *emissivity*, ϵ. It follows, then, that for a blackbody, $\epsilon = 1$, by definition. We may also define the ratio of radiant power absorbed by a body to the incident power as *absorptance* α. For a blackbody, $\alpha = 1$, and hence $\alpha_b = \epsilon_b$. It can be shown that even for nonblackbodies, as long as they are *opaque*, $\alpha = \epsilon$. Thus we may write

$$W = \epsilon W_b = \alpha W_b \quad (\textit{Kirchhoff's law}). \qquad (1\text{-}4)$$

All radiometric quantities depend on wavelength. In order to take this dependence into account, we define, for instance, *spectral emittance* W_λ as the amount of radiant power emitted by a unit area in a wavelength interval from λ to $\lambda + d\lambda$. It is found that *Kirchhoff's law* also applies to spectral emittances of opaque bodies:

$$W_\lambda = \epsilon_\lambda W_{\lambda b} = \alpha_\lambda W_{\lambda b}, \qquad (1\text{-}5)$$

or

$$\alpha_\lambda/\epsilon_\lambda = 1$$

In this form Kirchhoff's law may be said to state that at a given temperature a body absorbs most strongly radiation of that wavelength which it emits.

Planck's Law. Spectral dependence of radiative properties of a blackbody on temperature is described most accurately by *Planck's law*. This law in its simplest form expresses the *spectral energy density* u_ν, that is, the amount of radiant energy per unit volume of blackbody cavity per unit frequency interval as a function of temperature T and frequency ν by the following formula (for unpolarized radiation):

$$u_\nu = \frac{8\pi h\nu^3}{c^3(e^{h\nu/kT} - 1)}. \qquad (1\text{-}6)$$

This formula contains only fundamental constants c (the velocity of light), k (the *Boltzmann constant*, 1.380×10^{-16} erg/deg), and the *Planck constant* h; $h\nu$ is the quantum of radiant energy.

Planck's formula is often given in a form that applies to the more practical situation when the blackbody radiation is allowed to escape from the cavity through a small aperture. The rate of flow of the radiant energy per unit area of the aperture in wavelength interval $d\lambda$ at a wavelength λ, or spectral emittance, is then

$$W_{\lambda b}\, d\lambda = \frac{2\pi hc^2\, d\lambda}{\lambda^5(e^{hc/\lambda kT} - 1)}. \tag{1-7}$$

The constants $c_1 = 2\pi hc^2$ and $c_2 = hc/k$ are sometimes called the first and second radiation constants, respectively. Equation 1-7 is obtained from Eq. 1-6 if we recall that $\nu = c/\lambda$, $u_\nu\, d\nu = u_\lambda\, d\lambda$, and if we put $W_\lambda = \frac{1}{4}cu_\lambda$. The latter relation is obtained by integrating the energy flux in the forward direction over the hemispherical solid angle.

Planck's law describes the radiative properties of a blackbody exactly over the entire wavelength interval from 0 to ∞. An approximation valid for long wavelengths is obtained from Eq. 1-7 by expanding the exponential function and retaining only the first-order term:

$$W_{\lambda b} = \frac{c_1}{c_2}\frac{T}{\lambda^4}. \tag{1-8}$$

This is the *Rayleigh-Jeans law*, which becomes a good approximation only when the product λT is much greater than 100 000 micron degrees, that is, at very high temperatures or at very long wavelengths. The Rayleigh-Jeans law obviously cannot be correct at very short wavelengths, since it predicts $W_{\lambda b}$ to become infinitely large as λ approaches zero.

When Planck's formula (Eq. 1-7) is plotted graphically for various temperatures, one obtains a family of curves shown in Fig. 1-3. If we follow any particular curve (*isotherm*), we note that the spectral emittance is zero at $\lambda = 0$, then increases rapidly, goes through a maximum at a wavelength λ_{max}, and after passing it approaches zero at very long wavelengths. The higher the temperature, the shorter the wavelength at which the maximum occurs. In fact, by taking the derivative of Planck's formula with respect to λ and finding the maximum, we find that

$$\lambda_{max} = c_3/T. \tag{1-9}$$

The constant c_3 has a numerical value 2898μ deg. This is *Wien's Displacement law*, and it expresses mathematically the common observation that thermal radiators glow at dull red color when heated to relatively low temperatures (say about 1000°K), but then

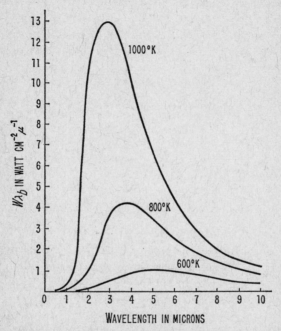

FIG. 1-3 **Blackbody spectral emittance curves according to Planck's law.**

appear more orange or yellow as their temperature is raised. Very hot stars (e.g., Sirius, 11 000°K) emit bluish-white light. At low temperatures the peak of the Planck's curve is in the infrared. At ambient temperature (about 300°K) $\lambda_{max} = 9.7\mu$; at the temperature of liquid nitrogen (77°K) $\lambda_{max} = 38\mu$.

By integrating the spectral emittance from $\lambda = 0$ to infinity, we obtain the total emittance,

$$W_b = \int_0^\infty W_{\lambda b}\, d\lambda = \sigma T^4, \qquad (1\text{-}10)$$

which is the *Stefan-Boltzmann law* mentioned before. The Stefan-Boltzmann constant is now obtained in terms of the fundamental constants $\sigma = 2\pi^5 k^4/15c^2 h^3 = 5.67 \times 10^{-5}$ erg cm^{-2} deg^{-4} sec^{-1}. Graphically, we note from Fig. 1-3 that W_b represents the area under the Planck's curve. It is apparent that this area increases very rapidly with temperature. It is often useful to know how much energy is emitted in a certain wavelength interval. This is obtained by taking the definite integral of $W_{\lambda b}\, d\lambda$ between the desired limits. In

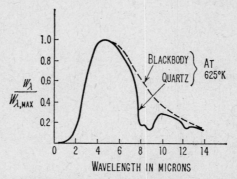

FIG. 1-4 Spectral emittance of a quartz crystal compared with that of a blackbody at the same temperature.

particular, it is found that the integrated emittance in the interval from λ_{max} to infinity is 75 percent of the total, while from $\lambda = 0$ to λ_{max} it is 25 percent of the total. For instance, a blackbody at 4500°K (e.g., a carbon arc) has λ_{max} at 0.65μ and emits 25 percent of its radiant power in the visible and ultraviolet regions of the spectrum while the greater part of its power is being radiated in the infrared.

NonBlackbody Emitters.   Thus far we have talked about radiation laws of a blackbody. Real bodies (materials) almost never comply with these laws over an extended wavelength interval, although they may approach the blackbody behavior in certain spectral regions. For instance, white paint which appears perfectly white in the visible becomes "gray" ($\epsilon \approx 0.5$) at about 2μ, and beyond 3μ wavelength it is almost "black" ($\epsilon \approx 0.9$). An example of a spectral emittance curve which differs greatly from that of a blackbody is shown in Fig. 1-4. This curve was obtained by measuring the emittance of a plate of clear, crystalline quartz heated to 625°K.

There are two principal reasons for which real bodies differ from the blackbody: first, they transmit some of the radiation (i.e., they are not opaque), and second, they reflect some of it. The first effect occurs only in bodies of a finite thickness, in particular if their intrinsic absorption is slight. Actually, it is the product of the thickness and the absorption coefficient which determines the transmittance of a body. (We shall define these terms later and see how they depend on each other.) Bodies of a very large ("infinite") thickness are always opaque. The second effect, reflection, is most conspicuous with metals, but it is present to some extent in all materials as long as they possess a well-defined surface boundary.

Let us first talk about metals, since they represent an extreme case of almost perfect opacity and high reflectivity. Of the radiation incident upon a metal surface, that fraction which is not absorbed will be reflected. If we define spectral *reflectivity* ρ_λ as the ratio of the reflected to the incident power at a given wavelength, we may write $\rho_\lambda + \alpha_\lambda = 1$, since the sum of the two fractions must add up to the whole. Now, because Kirchhoff's law ($\alpha_\lambda = \epsilon_\lambda$) applies to opaque bodies, we may also write

$$\epsilon_\lambda = 1 - \rho_\lambda. \tag{1-11}$$

In most metals spectral reflectivity is fairly high and does not vary much with wavelength. Consequently, the emissivity of metals is low and only slowly varying over a considerable wavelength interval. For instance, silver has $\epsilon_\lambda = 0.04$ at $\lambda = 1\mu$; 0.03 at 5μ; and 0.01 at 14μ.

Consider now a nonmetallic, semitransparent body—for simplicity, in the form of a flat plate. When the plate is heated, radiation generated within its volume must work its way toward the surfaces through the material in which it is partially absorbed (see Fig. 1-5). Moreover, when it arrives at the surface, some of it is reflected back into the interior (ray 2 in Fig. 1-5). The back-reflected radiation is again partially absorbed, but some of it arrives at the opposite surface, through which it mostly escapes; part of it is reflected back again (ray 3 in Fig. 1-5). Although the higher-order reflections are

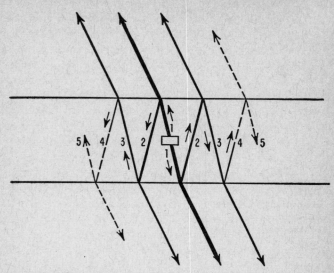

FIG. 1-5 Radiation emitted by a volume element of a transparent, absorbing plate.

getting weaker and weaker, they must all be added up when the total emittance of the plate is sought. When the resulting geometrical series is summed, the effective *emissivity* of a semitransparent plate is obtained as

$$\epsilon' = \frac{(1 - \rho_\lambda)(1 - \tau_\lambda)}{1 - \rho_\lambda \tau_\lambda} \quad (McMahon\text{'}s\ formula). \quad (1\text{-}12)$$

Here τ_λ denotes the *spectral transmittance*, defined as the ratio of the radiant power transmitted through the plate to the incident radiant power at a given wavelength λ. This formula represents a generalization of Kirchhoff's law. When the plate is opaque ($\tau_\lambda = 0$), the formula reduces to the original form of Kirchhoff's law (Eq. 1-11).

There are many other physical situations in which the radiation laws take on more complicated forms. For instance, propagation of heat through a layer of porous firebrick in a furnace is effected by a combination of radiation, absorption, diffuse scattering, and solid conduction. Or, on a more sublime scale, transfer of radiant energy from the interior of the sun toward the surface proceeds largely by a radiation-absorption process in a medium whose temperature, density, and other properties vary greatly with distance from the sun's center. In such cases the analysis becomes more involved, and advice is to be sought in advanced treatises listed among references given below.

REFERENCES

E. Scott Barr, "Historical Survey of the Early Development of the Infrared Spectral Region," Am. J. Phys. **28**, 42 (1960).

M. Planck, *The Theory of Heat Radiation* (Reprint) (Dover Publications, Inc., New York, 1959).

F. K. Richtmyer and E. H. Kennard, *Introduction to Modern Physics* (McGraw-Hill Book Company, New York, 1947).

H. O. McMahon, "Thermal Radiation from Partially Transparent Reflecting Bodies," J. Opt. Soc. Am. **40,** 376 (1950).

S. Chandrasekhar, *Stellar Structure* (Reprint) (Dover Publications, Inc., New York, 1957).

M. F. Zemansky, *Temperatures Very Low and Very High*, Van Nostrand Momentum Book No. 6 (D. Van Nostrand Company, Inc., Princeton N.J., 1964).

2   *Sources of Infrared Radiation*

THERMAL SOURCES

Cavity Radiators. A thermal radiation source of particular importance is the blackbody. A cavity of any shape made of any suitable opaque material heated to a uniform temperature generates blackbody radiation, the characteristics of which are determined solely by the temperature. In order to make use of the radiation produced in the cavity, we must provide an opening somewhere in the cavity wall. Theory demands that the area of the opening be small compared with the surface area of the cavity. If we use a small hole, the radiant flux output will be small. If we make the opening large so as to obtain greater radiant flux, the radiation may not have strictly the blackbody characteristics. In order to arrive at a satisfactory compromise we must make the cavity walls of a material of high emissivity. Then the radiative equilibrium can be attained with a small number of internal reflections, and it is permissible to use a fairly large orifice.

Cavity radiators are often made in the form of hollow cylinders or cones, as shown in Fig. 2-1. The average number of reflections a ray makes before emerging from the opening depends principally on the ratio of the hole area to the total area of the cavity. Then, for any given area ratio, the apparent emissivity of the radiator as seen from the orifice will be the nearer unity the higher the emissivity of the wall material. Apparent emissivity of cavities of simple shapes, such as spheres, cylinders, and cones, can be calculated by various methods. A typical set of curves, based on calculations by Gouffé, is shown in Fig. 2-2. Cavity area ratio is important not only in infrared radiometry, but also in pyrometric measurements. When

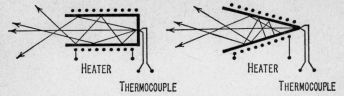

FIG. 2-1   Cylindrical and conical cavity radiators.

the temperature of an incandescent, nonblack solid is to be determined by a radiation pyrometer, a tiny reference cavity is usually provided in the body by drilling a blind hole in its surface. The degree of accuracy with which this reference cavity will approximate a blackbody may be estimated from diagrams such as shown in Fig. 2-2.

Cavities of the type shown in Fig. 2-1 may be made of metal (e.g., oxidized copper) or of a refractory ceramic material (e.g., aluminum

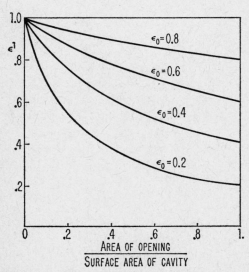

FIG. 2-2   Effective emissivity ε' of a cavity as a function of the opening ratio for various values of wall emissivity ε_0.

oxide) when higher operating temperatures are required. In the latter case, the walls may be blackened with a mixture of oxides of chrome, nickel, and cobalt. The cavity is usually heated by a resistance wire heater, and the temperature of the walls is measured by means of a thermocouple. For temperatures above 1500°K the radiator is sometimes made of graphite which can be heated by the passage of electric current through it. To prevent rapid oxidation, graphite must be protected by a blanket of inert gas, preferably argon. Unfortunately, emissivity of graphite is only about 0.5 in the middle infrared and still lower in the far infrared.

Solid Radiators. Cavity radiators such as described above are used only when the blackbody characteristics are essential. In practice, it is often satisfactory to use a "gray" radiator, provided it has reasonably high emissivity and a flat spectral emittance curve. In infrared spectrometers a convenient source of radiation is frequently realized by a rod of sintered silicon carbide (*globar*) which is heated by passing ac current through it. Average emissivity of this material is about 0.78 in the wavelength interval from 2 to 15μ with a flat maximum (0.85) at about 9μ. At a typical operating temperature of about 1300°K silicon carbide slowly oxidizes and eventually disintegrates. Another typical source often used in infrared spectrometers is the *Nernst glower*, made of a mixture of zirconium and yttrium oxides heated by passing current directly through it.

Metal radiators in the form of electric heaters are extensively used in industrial and household applications more for their convenience than for their emissivity, which is generally poor. Emissivity of tungsten, which is used to make the filaments of infrared heat lamps, is only 0.38 at 1μ, 0.10 at 2μ, 0.05 at 5μ, and about 0.04 at 10μ and beyond. Heat-resistant alloys which owe this property to the formation of protective oxides on their surface are somewhat better emitters. Nichrome, a typical alloy used extensively in electric radiators, heaters, toasters, and ovens, has emissivity about 0.85 at 1μ, slowly dropping to about 0.7 at 10μ.

The Sun. A thermal source of infrared radiation of greatest importance is the sun. Its total average radiant flux density above earth's atmosphere amounts to approximately 2.00 cal/cm^2 per minute, or about 1400 watts per square meter (the so-called *solar constant*). While the sun's radiation has a controlling and ever-present effect on all natural phenomena on the earth, its use in the laboratory is not very convenient. Nevertheless, solar furnaces have been built and occasionally used for research purposes. Here, high temperatures (up to about 4000°K) are obtained by concentrating the solar radiant flux by means of a large parabolic mirror. If it were not for earth's atmosphere, solar radiation would be found to conform very nearly, but not exactly, with Planck's curve of a blackbody radiator. If the solar emittance curve is made to fit with one of the curves of Fig. 1-3 in the near infrared, the corresponding temperature is found to be about 5600°K; if the fit is made in the

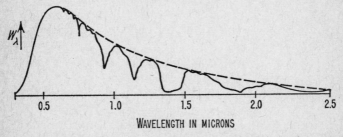

WAVELENGTH IN MICRONS

FIG. 2-3 Langley's curve of solar emittance. The dips in the curve are caused by absorption in the atmosphere, mostly by water vapor.

yellow-green, the temperature is about 6150°K. By attempting to make the fit in other spectral regions, still other temperatures would be found. The difficulty arises from the fact that we observe superimposed radiation coming from different gaseous layers of the solar surface which have different radiative properties, depending on depth. Spectral distribution of solar radiant energy as received after passing through earth's atmosphere has been accurately determined first by S. P. Langley (about 1880) in an extensive investigation sponsored by the Smithsonian Institute of Washington, D.C. The solar energy curve based on his measurements extending to 2.7μ is reproduced in Fig. 2-3. More recently, solar emittance measurements have been extended farther into the infrared, and numerous absorption bands resulting from atmospheric water, carbon dioxide, ozone, and other atmospheric gases have been identified.

NONTHERMAL SOURCES

If this section had been written three years ago, it would have been very brief. We would only have needed to point out that the emission spectra of many elements extend into the near infrared so that one can conveniently obtain infrared radiation at certain wavelengths from electrical discharge tubes. We would also have mentioned that the high-pressure mercury arc lamp emits, in addition to the near-infrared line spectrum, a strong, continuous radiation beyond about 100μ which makes it a useful source for far-infrared spectroscopy. Then, perhaps with a wishful note that microwave generators will some day be developed to the point that their output of higher harmonic frequencies will yield useful power in the submillimeter and far-infrared wavelength range, we would have come to the end.

The situation has changed with the discovery of quantum-electronic sources of radiation now commonly known as *lasers*. After a theoretical proposal of A. L. Schawlow and C. H. Townes (in 1958) the first laser was successfully demonstrated by T. H. Maiman (1960). Although the name laser refers to "light amplification by stimulated emission of radiation," most lasers are actually used as generators rather than amplifiers of radiation. The change from amplification to generation of self-sustained oscillations requires only that a part of the output power be fed back into the input with a proper phase and that the amplifier gain be large enough to make up for the losses. The feedback is effected by mirrors which reflect some of the radiation back into the laser medium; the distance between the mirrors, as related to the wavelength of the laser radiation, determines the phase.

The Ruby Laser. The essential part of the laser is the medium in which amplification of the radiation takes place. In the ruby laser this medium is a crystal of ruby, which is aluminum oxide (sapphire) colored pink by addition of a small percentage (0.05 percent) of chromium oxide. The ruby laser emits monochromatic radiation in the deep red, at about 0.693μ. The chromium ion, Cr^{3+}, is the active substance responsible for this particular emission. The sapphire crystal provides a suitable matrix in which the chromium ions are dissolved. Other active ions have been found to emit radiation at other wavelengths in the near infrared. In particular, ions of rare earths and of uranium in calcium fluoride or calcium tungstate host lattices make useful laser crystals. Neodymium gives laser activity to barium crown glass. The longest wavelength (2.36μ) recorded to date was obtained with the dysprosium-doped calcium fluoride crystal at 77°K (most laser crystals are operated at low temperatures).

The construction of the ruby laser is shown schematically in Fig. 2-4. The purpose of the flash lamp and the elliptical mirror shown in the picture is to deliver a pulse of intense radiation to the crystal rod. From the white spectrum of this "pumping" pulse some

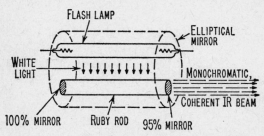

FIG. 2-4 Schematic diagram of a ruby laser.

chromium ions absorb energy in their blue-green absorption band and become promoted to a metastable *excited state*. Under normal circumstances these ions would return quickly to the *ground state*, ultimately emitting relatively weak fluorescence radiation in a broad band around 0.7μ. However, when the light pulse is so strong that the majority of chromium ions are momentarily raised to the excited state, the radiation from the ions undergoing transition *stimulates* the others which are still in the metastable state to join the process. It is the purpose of the mirrors at both ends of the ruby rod to reflect the radiation back into the interior of the crystal and thus generate the strong electromagnetic field necessary to induce the stimulated emission. The combined process of spontaneous and *stimulated emission* assumes avalanche proportions rapidly, and the emitted radiation, all of the same phase, emerges as a burst of radiation through one of the end mirrors made partially transparent for the purpose. The instantaneous power density of the burst may be of the order of many kw/cm². A special variety of a ruby laser has been developed which can deliver "giant pulses" up to several megawatt/cm². In the process of stimulated emission, the wavelength interval of the fluorescence band is greatly reduced, becoming typically of the order of 0.1Å. The narrow bandwidth is the result of a tuned-resonator effect of the end mirrors, which are accurately spaced so as to be an integral number of wavelengths apart. The radiation is coherent in the sense of having the same phase over a substantial part of the end area of the ruby rod. Since the wavefronts are plane, the emitted radiation propagates as a narrow beam the angular spread of which is limited solely by diffraction at the exit aperture.

Under favorable circumstances (which include very low temperature of the crystal) it is possible to maintain a steady state of excitation and continuous laser emission. This had been achieved first with the neodymium-calcium tungstate crystal operated at 77°K (the temperature of liquid nitrogen); the emitted radiation had a wavelength of 1.06μ.

In summary, we find the ruby laser to be an infrared source of highly monochromatic radiation and extremely high spectral emittance. High-power lasers can be operated intermittently, but at lower power levels continuous operation is possible. The radiation is coherent, narrowly collimated, and may be polarized, if the crystal is suitably oriented.

The Gas Laser. Amplification of radiation by stimulated emission can be obtained not only in crystals, but also in gases. In the gas laser, as originated by A. Javan in 1961, the working medium was a mixture of helium and neon at low pressure, ionized by an electric discharge. The role of the active element was then taken by neon in a situation somewhat analogous to that of chromium in the ruby laser. An excess of neon atoms in an excited state is generated by collisions with excited helium atoms which, in turn, have been excited by collision with electrons in the discharge. Excitation by electron collisions replaces the "pumping" with the flash of white light in ruby lasers. The stimulated emission is made possible by mirrors located at the ends of the gas discharge tube and accurately aligned so as to "tune in" a strong, standing-wave field along the tube. The operation of the gas laser is continuous, but its output power density is small compared with that of the pulsed ruby laser. The radiation is again coherent and highly monochromatic, and it may be polarized. Helium-neon gas lasers can emit a number of discrete wavelengths corresponding to the permitted radiative transitions among certain energy states of the excited neon atom. Only one of these wavelengths is in the visible red (0.633μ); all others are in the near infrared. Particularly strong laser emissions are obtained at 1.153μ and 3.39μ. Other gases and gas mixtures have been found to emit numerous other wavelengths, most of them in the infrared and extending as far as 57μ.

The Junction Laser. A third type of laser action was discovered recently in semiconductor diode junctions. It has been known for some time that when current is passed in the forward direction of a rectifying p-n junction the recombination of current carriers (electrons and holes) is accompanied by emission of infrared radiation. A particularly strong, narrow emission band at about 0.84μ was found in certain types of gallium arsenide diodes. When two opposite sides of the semiconductor junction wafer were polished flat and parallel, laser action was observed when the current density in the junction was raised above a certain threshold value (of the order of 10^3 to 10^4 amp/cm^2). Under these conditions the emitted radiation has the typical characteristics of a laser emission: it is highly monochromatic (about 0.5Å half-width), coherent, and very intense. Because of the heating associated with the necessary high current density, semiconducting junction lasers are usually operated with pulses of short duration and at very low temperatures (liquid nitrogen). The quantum efficiency of the semiconducting junction lasers is quite high, probably near unity; that is, nearly one photon is emitted for each electron (or hole) carried across the junction. The wavelength of the emitted radiation corresponds approximately to the energy gap which the carriers must cross between the top of the valency band and the bottom of the conduction band of the particular semiconductor used. In GaAs the energy gap is 1.45eV, corresponding (by Eq. 3-10) to a wavelength of 0.855μ; in InAs, the gap is $0.35eV$, and thus $\lambda \approx 3.5\mu$. Junction lasers seem to promise to become useful infrared sources, particularly where small size and high efficiency are required.

REFERENCES

American Institute of Physics, *Temperature, Its Measurement and Control* ("Emissivity of Solids," pp. 1313–1314) (Reinhold Publishing Corp., New York, 1941).

E. W. Treuenfels, "Emissivity of Isothermal Cavities," J. Opt. Soc. Am. **53**, 1162 (1963).

L. Goldberg, "Infrared Solar Spectrum," Am. J. Phys. **23**, 203 (1955).

B. A. Lengyel, *Lasers* (John Wiley & Sons, New York, 1963).

3 Detection of Infrared Radiation

THERMAL DETECTORS

We have no difficulty sensing the radiation when we stand in front of a blazing fire or lie down on the beach under midday sun. Things are different, however, when an astrophysicist wants to determine the temperature of the moon's surface by measuring its radiant emittance, or when a chemist uses an infrared spectrometer to determine the intensity of absorption bands caused by molecular vibrations in his compound. Under such circumstances we are dealing with exceedingly small radiant powers and have to use very sensitive instruments to detect and measure the radiation. Indeed, one of the principal problems in the history of infrared has been the search for detectors that would measure ever smaller amounts of radiant energy.

Thermal detectors have been conceived on the notion of the heating effect of radiation. When the radiation incident upon the receiver is absorbed, its temperature rises. The temperature increment may then be observed by measuring some material property which depends on temperature. There are three types of thermal detectors currently in use: pneumatic cells, thermocouples, and bolometers. Another type of thermal detector, the radiometer, once prominent in the hands of skillful experimenters such as E. Pringsheim, W. W. Coblentz, and C. G. Abbot, belongs only to history now. Typical of thermal detectors is their flat spectral response. If they have been properly blackened (e.g., by vacuum-deposited gold-black "smoke"), their responsivity remains nearly constant over a very wide range of wavelengths. The other class of radiation detectors, the photo- or quantum detectors, shows distinctly different spectral responses, characterized by a sharp cutoff in the long-wavelength range. We shall talk about photodetectors in the next section.

The Golay Cell. Pneumatic detectors make use of the large thermal expansivity of gas as the temperature-sensitive material property. William Herschel and other early investigators used various modifications of liquid-filled thermometers which, of course, did not allow very high sensitivity. Pneumatic detectors became practical only recently when it became possible to magnify the minute expansion

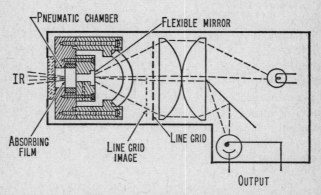

FIG. 3-1   Schematic diagram of a Golay pneumatic detector.

of gas, by means of electronics, and record it with electrical instruments. In the detector developed by H. V. Hayes (1936) the electrical read-out was obtained by means of variations of capacitance between a flexible membrane and a fixed plate. In the Golay cell (H. A. Zahl and M. Z. E. Golay, 1946), the displacements of a flexible membrane are magnified by optical means as shown in Fig. 3-1. The pneumatic cell contains a "black" absorber which is formed by a metallized collodion film having a surface resistivity very nearly equal to the impedance (377 ohms) that the electromagnetic waves encounter when propagating in free space. Radiation incident upon a film of this resistivity is absorbed rather than reflected. Expansion of gas resulting from heating of the film is transmitted through the central duct to a flexible collodion membrane at the back end of the device. The gas volume behind the flexible membrane is connected through a narrow channel of high impedance to the gas cell. In this way unwanted deflections of the membrane resulting from temperature differentials and slow drifts are canceled out. The flexible membrane, which is maintained taut under tension, is made reflective by a metallic coating so that it can reflect light from a light bulb on a photocell through a suitable optical system. This system contains a line grid, half of which is normally reflected on the other half. Initial adjustments are made so that when the membrane is undeflected, each bright line in the image coincides with an opaque line of the other half of the grid and no light passes to the photocell. Distention of the membrane causes some light to pass through, thus giving rise to electric current, which is amplified by electronic means. Because of the small masses involved, the Golay cell has a response time short enough (about 10 msec) to permit operation with "chopped" radiation. This offers the possibility of using ac amplification and synchronous rectification, a distinct advantage when dealing with weak signals in the presence of randomly fluctuating background "*noise*." The sensitivity of the Golay cell expressed in terms of radiation input power equal to the average noise power ("*noise equivalent power*," or N.E.P.) is quite high, typically about 5×10^{-11} watt at 1 cps bandwidth. The Golay cell is finding use mainly in spectroscopy, particularly in the far infrared.

   Thermocouples. Thermocouples represent historically the technological breakthrough which put detection of infrared radiation on a quantitative basis. Following the discovery of T. J. Seebeck (in 1825) that a temperature difference between the junctions of two different metals gives rise to a small voltage, L. Nobili constructed the first "thermopile" in 1830. This device was further improved by Nobili's friend, M. Melloni, who combined the thermopile with a sensitive galvanometer and obtained a highly useful infrared detector. Seebeck discovered very early the best combination of metals, namely bismuth and antimony, which remain in use, with slight modifications, to present time. The early thermopiles were made with a great number of junctions connected in series in order to multiply their output voltage. Actually, the only advantage of thermopiles was their higher resistance and, consequently, a better impedance match with the galvanometer. Since, with periodically modulated (*chopped*) radiation and ac amplification, impedance matching can be conveniently obtained with a transformer, thermocouples nowadays usually consist of single junctions.

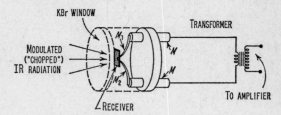

FIG. 3-2   Thermocouple of the wire type.

A typical thermocouple detector made of fine wires or strips is shown schematically in Fig. 3-2. Another currently used form of a thermocouple is shown in Fig. 3-3. The wires or pins M_1, M_2 are made of the special thermoelectric alloys (bismuth-tin and antimony-

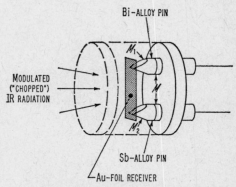

FIG. 3-3   Thermocouple of the pin type (Schwartz-Hilger).

cadmium), while the terminals and the rest of the circuitry are made of copper. In the wire thermocouple (Fig. 3-2), the blackened receiver is attached to the welded junction. In the pin-type thermocouple, the blackened gold-foil receiver forms the connection between the active metals. The junctions between the metals M_1, M_2 and the terminal metal M represent the "cold" junction, which is maintained at the ambient temperature while the "hot" junction is heated by the radiation. The additional thermoelectric voltages resulting from interposition of a third metal in the circuit (such as the metal M or the gold receiver between the pins in Fig. 3-3) cancel out when the temperatures of the additional junctions are equal. For small temperature differences ΔT between the hot and cold junctions, the thermoelectric voltage is found to be proportional to ΔT,

$$V = s \, \Delta T, \tag{3-1}$$

where s bears the historical but somewhat misleading name of *thermoelectric power*. It became customary to express thermoelectric powers with reference to a standard metal such as lead and to list the values for individual metals in microvolts per °C. One of the best combinations for radiation thermocouples is 97% Bi–3% Sb with 75%–25% Cd. The thermoelectric powers of these alloys are listed as -75 $\mu v/deg$ and $+112$ $\mu v/deg$ respectively; thus the couple would produce 187 μv for $\Delta T = 1$°C.

Responsivity of the Thermocouple. When radiant power flux W (watts/cm²) is incident upon a receiver of area A, its temperature rise ΔT is determined in the steady state by the rate at which it loses heat to the surroundings. There are three sources of heat loss: radiation, conduction in air, and conduction through the thermocouple wires. The combined effect of these processes may be characterized by an equivalent thermal conductance G, defined as the constant of proportionality in the relation:

$$WA = G \, \Delta T. \tag{3-2}$$

This simple linear relation (*Newton's cooling law*) is approximately valid for small values of ΔT; and we know that with radiation thermocouples the temperature differences almost never exceed a few millidegrees. Since we always want to obtain maximum ΔT with the given heat flux, we try to minimize G. Conduction of heat by the air is easily disposed of by evacuating the thermocouple enclosure. The other two sources of heat loss (radiation and conduction through wires) cannot be eliminated. The radiation conductance will be shown (in Chapter 6) to be

$$G_r = 4\sigma\epsilon A T^3, \tag{3-3}$$

where $\epsilon = \frac{1}{2}(\epsilon_f + \epsilon_b)$ is the resultant emissivity of the front and back sides of the receiver of area A. The conductance of the wires is

$$G_c = Ka/l, \tag{3-4}$$

where K is the conductivity of the metal, a the cross sectional area, and l the length of the wire. Since the conductances are in parallel, the resultant conductance is $G = G_r + G_c^{(1)} + G_c^{(2)}$, the superscripts (1) and (2) referring to the two wires of the thermocouple.

We may now inquire what determines the sensitivity of a thermocouple as a radiation detector. In order to avoid ambiguities that may result from using a word of common language, physicists introduced the term *responsivity*, meaning the ratio of the voltage developed by the detector to the radiant power (in watts) received by it. From Eqs. 3-1 and 3-2 we obtain for the responsivity of the thermocouple

$$r_0 = V/WA = s/G. \tag{3-5}$$

This expression is valid when by V is meant the open-circuit voltage of the thermocouple. A similar expression is obtained for the condition when the thermocouple is delivering current into a load of a given resistance, taking into account the voltage drop in the thermocouple wires; an additional, small correction must be applied to allow for the cooling of the junction caused by the current flowing through it (Peltier effect).

Experience has shown that optimum performance of a thermocouple detector is obtained when the radiative and conductive thermal conductances are made equal. Assuming $G_c^{(1)} = G_c^{(2)}$, we may write

$$r_0 = \frac{sl}{4Ka}. \tag{3-6}$$

This expression tells us what to do in order to obtain high responsivity in the steady state under continuous irradiation.

The situation is somewhat different when the thermocouple has to respond to rapidly varying radiation signals such as encountered when using chopped radiation. The *responsivity* $r(\omega)$ *for periodic signals* of frequency $\omega = 2\pi f$ is smaller than the dc responsivity r_0, and it is found to be reduced by a factor $(1 + \omega^2\tau^2)^{-1/2}$ so that

$$r(\omega) = r_0(1 + \omega^2\tau^2)^{-1/2}. \tag{3-7}$$

The quantity $\tau = C/G$ is called the *time constant* of the thermal response, and C is the heat capacity of the thermocouple. The function represented by Eq. 3-7 is plotted in Fig. 3-4. It is apparent

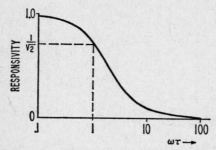

FIG. 3-4 Reduction of thermocouple responsivity when operating at a chopping frequency ω; τ is the time constant.

that at a frequency $\omega = 1/\tau = G/C$ the response is reduced to about 70 percent, while at a frequency ten times greater it is only a little more than 3 percent. In order to keep the response reasonably high even at high frequencies we must make the time constant small. That is, we must keep the heat capacity C small or make the conductance G large. However, large G would give small dc responsivity (Eq. 3-4); hence a compromise must be made. More complete theory of optimal design of thermocouples is to be found in references at the end of this chapter.

The best thermocouples commercially available have responsivities between 2 and 20 volts/watt and N.E.P. of the order of the order of 10^{-10} watt (for 1 cps bandwidth). Their receivers typically have surface areas of about 1 mm². The resistance of the thermocouples may lie between 10 and 100 ohms. Thermocouples are widely used in laboratory infrared instruments, particularly in spectrometers. Their limitations result from their fragility and relatively slow response.

The Bolometer. The bolometer was invented by Langley (1880) in the course of his researches on the energy distribution in solar spectrum. The temperature-dependent property utilized in the bolometer is the electrical resistivity of a metal or a semiconductor. Langley used fine platinum ribbons about 1μ thick and 200μ wide which were blackened to absorb the radiation. The temperature coefficient of resistivity (γ) in platinum is about 0.3 percent per °C, and values not much different from this figure are obtained with

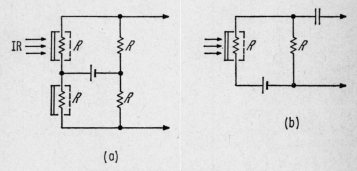

(a)

(b)

FIG. 3-5   Bolometer bridge circuits.

most other metals. Nickel and bismuth have been used on occasion, sometimes in the form of thin films produced by evaporation *in vacuo.* Much greater values of γ are obtained in semiconductors.

The change of resistance caused by heating of the bolometer element is converted into a voltage by connecting the bolometer in a Wheatstone bridge circuit, as shown in Fig. 3-5a. Two identical elements are used, one being exposed to the radiation while the other, shielded from radiation, serves to compensate for slow changes (drifts) in the ambient temperature. The bridge which was initially balanced becomes unbalanced when the bolometer element is irradiated. Langley and other early investigators used sensitive galvanometers to measure the unbalance current. When the radiation is periodically variable, the galvanometer may be replaced by an ac amplifier. In this case a simpler circuit is often used (Fig. 3-5b). Analysis shows that the dc responsivity of the bolometer can be expressed (approximately, for small signals) by

$$r_0 = \gamma Ri/G, \tag{3-8}$$

in which i denotes the current passed through the bolometer of resistance R by the battery. G is the thermal conductance defined in the same way as in Eqs. 3-2, 3-3, and 3-4. Equation 3-8 suggests that for highest responsivity the current i be made as high as possible. The limit to it is set by the increase in current-generated noise about which we shall talk later.

The response of a bolometer to ac signals is governed by Eq. 3-7. Just as with the thermocouple, ac response of the bolometer can be improved only by making the time constant shorter. In semiconducting bolometers designed for fast response, thermal conductance is purposely increased by depositing the resistance element on a solid substrate of high conductivity (e.g., sapphire).

The first successful semiconducting bolometer, or *thermistor*, was developed by W. H. Brattain and J. A. Becker at Bell Telephone Laboratories (1946). The active element is a thin flake of a semiconducting material consisting of a mixture of metal oxides (Mn, Co, Ni). The resistance coefficient of this material may be as high as 4 percent per °C. Thermistor bolometers are commercially fabricated in a compact form of small cells provided with an infrared-transmitting window or with a focusing hemispherical lens to which they are attached (*immersed bolometer*). Thermistor bolometers have high resistance (about 2 megohms), responsivity from 40 to 1000 volts/watt, and N.E.P. (for 1 cps bandwidth) of the order of 10^{-10} watt. Metal bolometers have low resistance, usually between 10 and 100 ohms; responsivity between 2 and 10 volts/watt; and N.E.P. of about 10^{-10} watt (for 1 cps bandwidth). Time constants of both thermistor and metal wire bolometers vary between 2 and 20 msec.

All of the detectors we have talked about thus far are operated at room temperature. However, it was recognized quite early that the performance of nonmetallic bolometers improves greatly with operation at low temperatures. Progress in cryogenic technology made it possible to consider practical use of liquid-cooled devices down to the temperature of liquid helium (4.2°K). Some work has been done with carbon resistor bolometers at cryogenic temperatures, and even superconducting bolometers have been tried. However, none of these devices became practical. One of the first successful low-temperature bolometers was described by F. J. Low in 1961. The bolometer element used in this detector was a thin wafer cut from a single crystal of gallium-doped germanium. The N.E.P. of this detector was reported to be 5×10^{-13} watt at 2°K and 1 cps bandwidth; this is about 100 times better than with bolometers operated at room temperature. The responsivity was 4500 volt/watt, resistance about 5×10^5 ohms, and time constant about 0.4 msec. The spectral response of Ga- or Zn-doped germanium bolometers remains substantially flat from about 2μ into the far infrared and millimeter waves. The ultimate limit of performance of bolometers of this type is set by the radiation noise, that is, the random fluctuations in the number of photons arriving at the detector.

NONTHERMAL DETECTORS

In nonthermal detectors radiation is converted into electrical signals directly rather than via some temperature-dependent process. Because of the nature of this conversion process nonthermal detectors are sometimes also called *quantum detectors* or *photodetectors*. Non-thermal detectors are basically of the *photoconductive* or *photoemissive* type. In all quantum detectors the release or transfer of charge carriers (e.g., electrons) can be directly associated with absorption of quanta of radiation. This is apparent from the fact that their spectral response curve drops sharply to zero at the long-wavelength side at some well-defined wavelength. Since the energy of the radiation quantum is inversely proportional to the wavelength associated with it (Eq. 1-3), we may conclude that the disappearance of photo-electric activity at some long wavelength indicates the energy of the quanta to be insufficient to set the electrons free. In photoconductive solids the electron becomes "free" for the conduction process only when the energy it gained from the absorbed quantum exceeds a certain level known as the energy gap (E_g), which is familiar from the band theory of semiconductors. Hence the photoeffect can occur only at energies greater or wavelengths shorter than a limit λ_c given by

$$\lambda_c = hc/E_g. \tag{3-9}$$

Solid state physicists measure E_g in electron volts rather than ergs. One electron volt is the energy which a particle carrying one unit of elementary charge (4.80×10^{-10} electrostatic units, or 1.62×10^{-19} coulombs) acquires over a potential difference of one volt. In these terms one electron volt is equivalent to 1.60×10^{-13} erg, and the Planck constant has a value $h = 4.135 \times 10^{-15}$ eV sec. Equation 3-9 may then be written as

$$\lambda_c = \frac{1.24 \times 10^{-4} \text{ eV cm}}{E_g}. \tag{3-10}$$

According to this formula, energy of one electron volt corresponds to that of radiation of 1.24-micron wavelength. Energy gaps of some materials that are of significance in photoconductive detectors and their corresponding long-wavelength limits are listed in Table 3-1.

TABLE 3-1   *Energy Gaps and Long-Wavelength Limits of Selected Materials*

Material	E_g (at 300°K), eV	λ_c, micron
Se	2.1	0.59
Si	1.1	1.13
Ge	0.68	1.82
Te	0.34	3.65
PbS	0.40	3.10
PbTe	0.31	4.00
PbSe	0.25	4.95
InSb	0.18	6.90

Semiconducting Photoconductors. All of the materials in Table 3-1 are so-called *intrinsic semiconductors*, that is, those in which the gap energy is determined by the nature of the material itself rather than by added impurities. Sometimes small amounts of impurities are present in the semiconducting material either naturally or by intentional addition (doping). These then are the so-called *impurity semiconductors*. Impurity atoms which may give off an electron when incorporated into the host crystal (e.g., As in Si) produce a material with a slight excess of (negative) electrons (*n-type* semiconductors). Other atoms tend to accept electrons from the host material and thus produce an excess of positive "holes" (*p-type* semiconductors). Intermediate energy levels associated with impurities allow electron excitation to take place at smaller quantum energies than those required with the intrinsic semiconductors. Thus, by suitable doping the long-wavelength limit can be pushed quite far into the infrared. For instance, germanium doped with gallium is a p-type semiconductor with an impurity energy level of 0.065 eV, which makes it useful as a photoconductive detector to about 19μ wavelength.

When a semiconductor is illuminated with radiation of quantum energy (hc/λ) greater than E_g, some electrons are excited to the conduction band, and corresponding numbers of holes are left behind and made mobile in the valence band. Thus the number of charge carriers is increased, and the conductivity of the material becomes temporarily greater. The responsivity of a photoconductive detector is then proportional to the excess of charge carrier concentration Δn. The steady state concentration is reached when the rate of generation of electrons by absorbed photons is equal to the rate at which they are removed from the conduction process by recombination with holes and by other mechanisms (trapping). If Q is the number of photons arriving per unit area per sec, α the optical absorption coefficient, and η the probability of electron excitation resulting from absorption of a photon (quantum efficiency), then the rate at which electrons are generated per unit volume is $\alpha\eta Q$. The recombination rate is directly proportional to the excess concentration Δn and inversely proportional to the average electron *lifetime t* in the conduction band. Thus in steady state $\Delta n/t = \alpha\eta Q$, and the (dc) responsivity is proportional to $\Delta n/Q$,

$$r_0 \propto (\Delta n/Q) = \alpha\eta t. \tag{3-11}$$

In intrinsic semiconductors the absorption coefficient on the short-wavelength side of the energy gap is very high, typically of the order of 10^{-4} cm. The radiation intensity or photon density decreases exponentially with the distance into the material. Consequently, there is no use making the semiconducting photodetector much thicker than α^{-1}, that is, about one micron. Equation 3-11 states that for high responsivity both carrier lifetime and quantum efficiency should be high. How to achieve this condition with given materials and doping elements is a rather complicated subject matter which would go beyond the scope of this book.

Under certain circumstances radiation absorbed in semiconductors can generate dc voltage rather than mere change of resistance. Devices based on this effect are called *photovoltaic cells*. Essential for their operation is the existence of a so-called barrier layer similar to that existing in semiconducting rectifier diodes. The barrier may be formed either at a metal-semiconductor contact or at a junction between n- and p-type semiconductors. The function of the barrier layer is to separate the oppositely-charged carriers and to maintain the potential difference generated under illumination. When the rectifying junction is biased so as to block the current flow, the radiation-generated charge carriers can produce secondary carriers within the collector region, thus multiplying the photocurrent. Devices based on this effect are called phototransistors.

Separation of photoelectrically produced charge carriers can also be assisted by a magnetic field applied in a direction perpendicular to the current flow (*photo-electromagnetic* or PEM *detectors*). Photoelectric processes in semiconductors are very complex and not yet fully understood in every aspect. It took about fifty years, following the accidental discovery of photoconductivity of selenium by Willoughby Smith (in 1873), before the understanding of photoelectric phenomena began to emerge from the confusing facts. By the 1930s the basic theory of photoconductivity in semiconductors was established roughly in the form that we know today, largely by the efforts of R. W. Pohl and his co-workers (in particular, B. Gudden) in Göttingen. In the intervening years sporadic research produced discoveries of photoconductivity in cuprous oxide (by A. H. Pfund, 1916) and in various minerals including Sb_2S_3, Bi_2S_3 and PbS (by T. W. Case, 1917). Case later discovered the importance of oxygen as a desirable impurity in thallium sulfide (Tl_2S) and developed the "thalofide" cell into a highly-sensitive detector useful in the visible and in the near infrared. The great push for high performance and extended long-wavelength limit started in the 1940s when film-type lead sulfide photoresistive detectors were developed almost simultaneously in Germany, Great Britain, and the USA. Other "lead salt" detectors, PbTe and PbSe, followed shortly thereafter; in the 1950s appeared indium antimonide, and still later, various impurity-type semiconducting photodetectors. Spectral response characteristics of these detectors are shown in Fig. 3-6. The importance of operating photoconductive detectors at low temperatures was quickly realized, with a threefold benefit gained from it: higher responsivity, longer wavelength cutoff, and

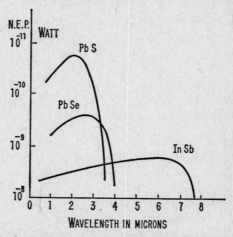

FIG. 3-6 Typical spectral response of photoconductive semiconducting detectors (at room temperature, 800 cps chopping frequency, 1 cps bandwidth and 0.1 cm² area.

decreased thermal noise. The effect of cooling with dry ice (195°K) and liquid nitrogen (77°K) is shown in Fig. 3-7.

The construction of photoconductive cells is somewhat similar to that of thermistor bolometers. The film of lead sulfide, selenide, or telluride is deposited (either chemically or by vacuum evaporation) on a suitable insulating substrate and provided with metallic contacts. The heat conduction into the substrate determines the response time, which is usually quite short (about 100 μsec or less). This permits high chopping or scanning frequencies, typically up to several hundred cps.

Lead sulfide cells are available commercially in various forms and sizes; the active surface area is typically about 0.1 cm². Chemically prepared cells are quite stable and may be used even without protective windows. Their resistance, which at room temperature is between 10^5 and 10^6 ohms, increases substantially on cooling. The responsivity is high, typically about 5000 volts/watt, and N.E.P. (at 1 bandwidth) is of the order of 10^{-11} watt at the peak of the spectral response curve (about 2.2μ). Some improvement in performance is

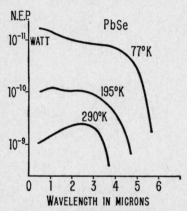

FIG. 3-7   Effect of cooling on the spectral response of a lead selenide photoconductive detector.

obtained on cooling, the optimum temperature being about $-100°C$ (the temperature of dry ice).

The lead selenide cells improve much more on cooling, and their optimum performance is obtained at the temperature of liquid nitrogen (Fig. 3-7). The same or still lower temperatures are required for best performance of lead telluride cells. Liquid-cooled cells are often constructed integrally with a small Dewar flask which serves both as a container for the refrigerant and as a vacuum envelope for the photoconducting film (Fig. 3-8). The requirement for liquid nitrogen cooling and the inconveniences associated with its use detract considerably from the utility of PbSe and PbTe cells.

Indium antimonide detectors are made of thin strips of single crystal material cemented to a suitable substrate. Their resistance is low, typically about 100 ohms, their responsivity is about 1 volt/watt, and their N.E.P. at room temperature is about 10^{-9} watt at the peak of the spectral response curve (about 6.8μ). The performance figures improve by more than an order of magnitude on cooling with liquid nitrogen, but, contrary to the lead salt cells, the

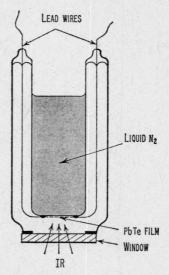

FIG. 3-8   Lead telluride photoconductive detector cooled with liquid nitrogen.

long-wavelength cutoff shifts to shorter wavelengths (to about 6μ from 7.7μ). The response time is very short, often less than 1 μsec. The InSb detectors are rugged, stable, and generally very useful in the spectral range from the visible to about 7μ.

Photovoltaic semiconducting cells have been made with selenium, lead sulfide, silicon, and other materials. The silicon p-n junction photovoltaic cell is widely used as an efficient converter of solar energy, but its response curve cuts off in the near infrared at about 1.1μ. In general, the performance of photovoltaic cells as infrared detectors is inferior to that of photoconductive cells, and therefore they are not widely used.

Photoemissive Detectors. This chapter would not be complete without a mention of photoemissive detectors even though their spectral response remains limited to the very near infrared. Photoemission of electrons from metals into vacuum is governed by the same basic law (Eq. 3-9) as the photoelectric excitation of electrons into the conduction band in semiconductors. The energy barrier that an electron has to cross when ejected from the metal into vacuum is

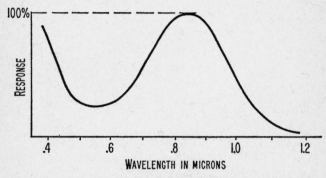

Fig. 3-9 Spectral response of the Ag-O-Cs photocathode.

called photoelectric "work function," and it too is measured in electron volts. Among the elements, alkali metals have the lowest work functions, and the lowest of them belongs to metallic cesium (about 1.9 eV). This value corresponds to a long-wavelength cutoff at 0.63μ, not good enough for use even in the nearest infrared. In semiconductors and composite surfaces, lower values of work function can be obtained because electrons may be excited from intermediate impurity levels. Most successful of these composite materials is the silver-oxygen-cesium photocathode discovered by L. R. Koller in 1929. Spectral response of this photocathode, which is designated in the electron tube standards as S-1, is shown in Fig. 3-9. The reason that the long-wavelength limit extends so far into the infrared is not entirely clear, but it is believed that photoemission actually takes place in a layer of cesium oxide, which is an *n*-type semiconductor with silver acting as a donor impurity. This impurity introduces a shallow level of about 0.3 eV, and the work function of the surface appears to be depressed below 1 eV; the two effects combined would allow photoemission at wavelengths longer than 1μ.

Silver-oxygen-cesium photocathodes are most often utilized in photomultiplier tubes (Fig. 3-10) in which amplification is obtained by the process of secondary emission in a cascade fashion. In this way a gain of up to 10^6 may be obtained directly in the tube, without the aid of an amplifier.

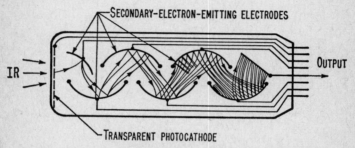

FIG. 3-10   **Photomultiplier tube with end-on cathode.**

The photomultiplier tube is by far the most sensitive detector of radiation known. Its responsivity at the peak of its spectral response curve may be as high as 10^{10} volts/watt. The limit to the minimum detectable power is set by the fluctuations (*shot noise*) in the spontaneous emission from the photocathode. When amplified and time-integrated, the shot noise manifests itself as a background current (dark current). By cooling the photocathode with liquid nitrogen dark current can be reduced to values as low as 10^{-17} amp/cm². Under such conditions N.E.P. of the order of 10^{-16} watt have been reported. Photocathodes of the Ag-O-Cs type have been used in various infrared detecting and imaging devices such as image converters and TV vidicons. Photomultiplier tubes have very short response times, typically about 10^{-8} sec.

LIMITS OF DETECTION OF RADIATION

Signal and Noise. All of us have probably been frustrated at some time by being unable to tune in a weak or distant television station on our receiver. The audio signal seemed to have been drowned in the hissing noise, and the video signal was barely perceptible through the "snow" on the screen. Such disturbances have come to be known as "noise," by analogy with acoustic noise. Some of the noise originated in the space between the transmitter and the receiving antenna, but most of it was generated right in our receiver when the gain was high. The infrared spectroscopist finds himself in a similar situation when he is looking for a weak spectral band and, instead of a clear-cut recording, obtains a trace in which the noise and the signal (i.e., the band sought) are scrambled together, as shown in Fig. 3-11.

Noise is characterized by its random fluctuations in amplitude, frequency, and phase. In order to compare it with the signal of constant amplitude and frequency, we use the square root of the noise amplitude squared (rms value), and we define the *signal-to-noise ratio S* as

$$S = V_s/V_n. \tag{3-12}$$

In this case V_s designates the rms value of the signal voltage and V_n the rms value of the noise voltage. Considering the noise originating in the detector itself, we find that there are four principal kinds: Johnson noise, current noise, shot noise, and radiation noise.

Johnson noise results from statistical thermal fluctuations of electron density in a conductor. In a conductor of resistance R at absolute temperature T the rms value of voltage fluctuations observable by a detector that responds only to a narrow frequency band of width Δf (cps) is given by the expression

$$\Delta V_J = (4kTR \, \Delta f)^{1/2}. \tag{3-13}$$

The rms value of the Johnson noise voltage does not depend on the frequency at which it is being measured; this kind is called *white noise.* Johnson noise voltage appears at the terminals of any kind of resistor even when there is no current flowing through it. This type of noise is common to all radiation detectors using resistive elements. Equation 3-13 was implied in a slightly different form by A. Einstein in 1906 in his theory of Brownian motion. The present name became

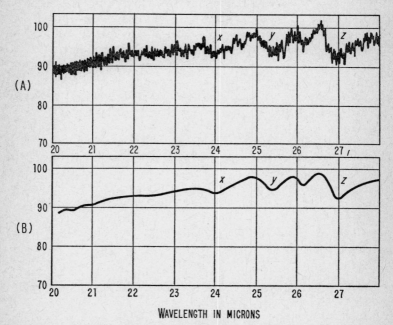

WAVELENGTH IN MICRONS

FIG. 3-11 Recording of a part of IR spectrum at low signal-to-noise ratio; (B) smoothed curve based on (A) with a doubtful band at x.

established after J. B. Johnson and H. Nyquist derived it (in 1928) from the point of view of circuit theory. The formula does not contain the electronic charge; this reminds us of the fact that Johnson noise is of statistical origin and has nothing to do with the corpuscular nature of electricity.

Current noise appears as a voltage fluctuation in excess of Johnson noise when current flows through a conductor. This is the case in thermocouples, bolometers, and photoconductive detectors. Current noise is most pronounced in semiconductors, nonmetallic conductors (e.g., carbon resistors), and very thin metal films. It seems to have various contributory causes, such as fluctuations in generation and recombination of charge carriers in semiconductors or contact resistance noise in heterogeneous materials. The rms value of current noise voltage often obeys an empirical relation of the form

$$\Delta V_c = CRi(\Delta f/f)^{1/2}, \tag{3-14}$$

where i is the current passing through the resistance R, and C is a constant. The current noise spectrum is not "white," but rather we might say it tends to be "red" because of the inverse frequency term under the square root; the current noise power (proportional to $\Delta V_c{}^2$) is greater when measured at lower frequencies. That is why it is preferable to operate photoconductive detectors at high chopping frequencies.

Shot noise observed in vacuum tubes and photomultipliers arises from the fact that the electric charge is transported by elementary particles of a discrete charge ($e = 1.60 \times 10^{-19}$ coulomb). The rms value of the shot noise current fluctuation of an average emission current i_0 is given by

$$\Delta i = (2ei_0 \, \Delta f)^{1/2}, \tag{3-15}$$

which was derived by Wilhelm Schottky in 1918. Shot noise has a white spectrum like the Johnson noise.

Radiation noise results from the statistical fluctuation of the radiant energy as it is being received and re-emitted by the detector; we may say that it results from the random rate of arrival of photons. In the approximation of classical statistics, the fluctuation $\Delta \bar{n}$ in number of photons arriving at a unit area of irradiated surface is proportional to the square root of the average photon flux n, that is,

$$\Delta \bar{n} \propto n^{1/2}.$$

In a given radiant power flux W (erg cm^{-2} sec^{-1}) the number of photons of energy $h\nu$ in a frequency band from ν to $\nu + \Delta \nu$ is

$$n = \frac{W_\nu \, \Delta \nu}{h\nu}. \tag{3-16}$$

For a blackbody radiation, W_ν can be obtained from W_λ using Eq. 1-7. It can then be shown that the rms value of the fluctuations of the total radiant flux W is

$$\Delta \overline{W} = 4(WkT\,\Delta \nu)^{1/2}. \qquad (3\text{-}17)$$

If the receiver has an area A and emissivity ϵ, $W = A\epsilon\sigma T^4$, according to the Stefan-Boltzmann law (Eq. 1-10). We may then rewrite Eq. 3-17 as

$$\Delta \overline{W} = 4(A\epsilon\sigma kT^5\,\Delta f)^{1/2}. \qquad (3\text{-}18)$$

We have substituted Δf for $\Delta \nu$ so as to be consistent with our current usage of letter f for the frequency of the amplifier system while retaining ν for the frequency of the radiation. In this instance they are, of course, one and the same. It is to be noted, however, that neither ν nor f appears in Eqs. 3-17 and 3-18. The radiation noise power fluctuation is, therefore, independent of frequency or wavelength; it is a white noise spectrum.

Smallest Detectable Signal. Let us calculate the radiation noise in a thermal detector which is so perfect that it generates no other noise whatever. Assume that the receiver has an area $A = 0.1$ cm², emissivity $\epsilon = 1$, and that it is at temperature $T = 300°$K equal to that of the surroundings; assume further that the amplifier system used has a bandwidth $\Delta f = 1$ cps. Then, according to Eq. 3-18 the rms noise power in the detector will be 1.74×10^{-11} watt. This power will generate certain noise voltage ΔV_n in the detector, depending on its responsivity. A signal having the same power will generate a signal voltage ΔV_s of the same rms value, thus giving a signal-to-noise ratio $S = \Delta V_s/\Delta V_n = 1$. This is what we call the noise-equivalent-power (N.E.P.) of a detector. Hence, the lowest N.E.P. of an ideal thermal detector as determined by the radiation noise alone (at $300°$K) is 1.74×10^{-11} watt. We recall that typical thermocouples and bolometers operating at ambient temperatures had an N.E.P. of the order of 10^{-10} watt.

The noise-equivalent power of a thermal detector depends, according to Eq. 13-18, on the square root of the receiver area A and the bandwidth Δf. The factor $(A\,\Delta f)^{1/2}$ crops up when similar calculations are made for other types of detectors considering the particular type of noise which determines their limiting N.E.P. For this reason Clark Jones, who has given much thought to the problem of proper evaluation of performance of various radiation detectors, introduced a quantity called *detectivity*, D^* (D-*star*), defined as

$$D^* = (A \, \Delta f)^{1/2}/\text{N.E.P.} \tag{3-19}$$

Being an inverse quantity to N.E.P., D^* assumes higher values for "better" detectors. It also removes the dependence on A and Δf when detectors of various areas and at different bandwidths are compared. D^* has become widely accepted among infrared technologists, but it is by no means the only or universally appropriate characteristic of a radiation detector. Among some of its deficiencies one perceives immediately its dependence on the nature of the radiation used for its determination. In the case of an ideal thermal detector which had a perfectly flat spectral response, it was sufficient to state at what blackbody temperature the measurement of N.E.P. or D^* was made. The situation is more complicated with photoconductors whose spectral response is nonlinear and typically drops to zero at the long-wavelength cutoff point. The D^* is then wavelength dependent and consequently bears the usual subscript, D^*_λ. D^*_{max} is usually quoted at the peak of the spectral response curve, but intercomparison among different detectors becomes difficult when determinations have been made with blackbody sources of different temperatures.

REFERENCES

R. A. Smith, F. E. Jones, and R. P. Chasmar, *Detection and Measurement of Infrared Radiation* (Oxford University Press, London, 1957).

T. S. Moss, *Optical Properties of Semiconductors* (Butterworths, London, 1959).

R. De Waard and E. M. Wormser, "Description and Properties of Various Thermal Detectors," Proc. Inst. Radio Eng. **47,** 1508 (1959).

R. Clark Jones, "Noise in Radiation Detectors" and "Phenomenological Description of the Response and Detecting Ability of Radiation Detectors," Proc. Inst. Radio Eng. **47,** 1481 and 1495 (1959).

4   *Materials and Optics*

OPTICAL PROPERTIES OF SOLIDS

Infrared radiation was discovered in a search for a new optical material. Herschel was looking for a substance that would stop the solar radiation from heating the lenses of the telescope. Although he did not find the material he was looking for, he discovered the cause of the effect. He and his contemporaries did not realize that the newly discovered thermal radiation was transmitted only to a limited extent by glass, the only optical material available to them. In fact, some of the early controversies about the very existence of thermal radiation resulted from the fact that different investigators used prisms made of different kinds of glass. It was found much later that crown glass was cutting off in the near infrared (about 2μ) while flint (lead) glass transmitted as far as about 4.5μ. This became clear only after infrared spectrometers had been developed and the wavelength scale established far enough into the infrared.

The first material truly transparent to the infrared was discovered by Melloni. It was the naturally occurring rock salt (NaCl), which was available in large enough natural crystals to become useful for making lenses and prisms. It remained the principal optical material for infrared optics for over a hundred years. Several other naturally occurring crystalline materials have been introduced since, including quartz (SiO_2), fluorite (CaF_2) and sylvite (KCl). Much later, in the 1940s, the art of growing synthetic crystals was mastered, and a whole variety of materials that do not exist in nature, transparent far into the infrared, became available.

Refraction, Absorption, and Dispersion.   Optical properties of transparent media are conveniently characterized by two constants: the refractive index n and the absorption coefficient α. The refractive index may be defined by *Snell's law of refraction,*

$$n = \sin \phi / \sin \chi, \tag{4-1}$$

where ϕ denotes the angle of incidence at a plane boundary between vacuum and the medium and χ is the angle at which the rays are refracted into the medium. On wave theory Snell's law follows from the fact that the velocity of propagation in the medium differs from that in vacuum, c. The refractive index is then the ratio $n = c/v$. The *absorption coefficient* α is the factor in the exponent of *Lambert-Bouguer's law* which describes the attenuation of radiation in absorbing medium as a function of distance,

$$I = I_0 e^{-\alpha x}, \quad \text{or} \quad T_a = e^{-\alpha x}. \tag{4-2}$$

Here I_0 denotes the intensity of the radiation incident upon the boundary, and I is the radiation at the distance x in the medium. $T_a = I/I_0$ is called *transmittance*. Sometimes another quantity called the *extinction index* (k) is used; it is defined by the relation

$$k = \alpha \lambda / 4\pi, \tag{4-3}$$

where λ is the wavelength measured outside the medium.

Actually n and α are not constants, as in some regions they are strongly dependent on wavelength. If we measure the spectral dependence of n and α of various solids over an extended wavelength interval, we find always a typical pattern similar to that shown in Fig. 4-1. As we move toward longer wavelengths, the refractive index drops sharply to a minimum and then rises suddenly to a peak from which it gradually decreases again on the long wavelength side. At the same time, the absorption coefficient goes through a peak centered at a wavelength about midway between the minimum and maximum of the refractive index. The wavelength region over which this double act extends is called the *dispersion band*. Two dispersion bands shown in the figure represent a typical situation encountered with crystals of diatomic compounds such as NaCl, KBr, etc. Crystals of more complex composition and noncubic structure, like quartz $(SiO)_2$ or calcite $(CaCO_3)$, show several dispersion bands.

We are concerned here only with the bands in the infrared region. From the band lying in the ultraviolet region infrared spectroscopists seem to care only about the downward sloping part of the refractive index curve because it is what makes their prism spectrographs work. Obviously, as long as n varies with wavelength the angle of refraction of different components of the radiation falling upon the prism will also vary depending on wavelength. The rays of various wavelengths will thus be thrown apart or dispersed—hence the name. Unfortunately, where dispersion is really great the absorption becomes prohibitively large, and so the practically useful region remains

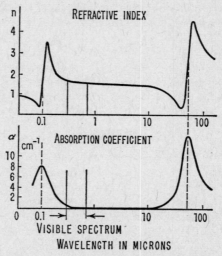

FIG. 4-1 Dependence of refractive index and absorption coefficient of a typical ionic crystal (NaCl) on wavelength.

limited to the central part between the ultraviolet and infrared bands.

The characteristic way the refraction and absorption bands are related to each other is no coincidence; it is merely a manifestation of two different aspects of the same phenomenon. The reader familiar with the analysis of electrical circuits will recognize in the dispersion band the characteristics of resonance. The upper curve in Fig. 4-1 is reminiscent of the variation of phase angle with wavelength, while the lower curve corresponds to the variation of current or voltage amplitude. What kind of resonance is it that manifests itself in this way in optical materials? At a risk of some oversimplification, we may say that the infrared dispersion bands result from resonances in lattice vibrations; the ultraviolet dispersion bands, from resonances of weakly bound electrons in the atomic valence bands.

Materials other than transparent insulators show somewhat different behavior. Semiconductors, which have electrical properties halfway between those of metals and insulators, seem to be that way in their optical properties also. Typical semiconductors look

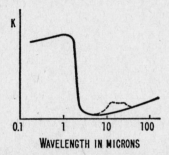

FIG. 4-2 Wavelength dependence of the absorption coefficient of an intrinsic semiconductor (Ge).

almost like metals and are found to be quite opaque in the visible. In the infrared they are, like insulators, transparent. We have already learned why this is so. In the visible range of spectrum the energy of light quanta is high enough to excite electrons from the valence band into the conduction band. Thus the material becomes conducting and reflects and absorbs radiation like a metal. At longer wavelengths the energy of infrared quanta is insufficient to cause photoconductivity, and the absorption becomes so small that the material behaves more like a transparent insulator. Because of this state of affairs the absorption curve of semiconductors has a typical course shown in Fig. 4-2. The absorption coefficient is high in the visible range and drops sharply at a wavelength corresponding to that of the gap energy. After that it remains low over a fairly wide wavelength range. At still longer wavelengths it tends to rise again because of the presence of some "free" carriers in the conduction band. Impurities may cause some weaker absorption bands to appear in the intermediate wavelength range. The refractive index of semiconductors is rather high ($n = 4$ in germanium) and does not vary much with the wavelength. By and large, semiconductors show nowhere in the infrared the dispersion bands so typical of ionic crystals. The reason for it is precisely that they are not ionic, but rather covalent in their chemical constitution. Since there are no electric dipoles built in with their structure, the lattice vibrations do not interact with the electromagnetic waves and the resonance effects are not observed.

Reflection. When radiation is incident normally at a plane boundary between vacuum and a semi-infinite transparent solid, most of it penetrates and eventually becomes absorbed, but some of it is reflected back. If the absorption is very weak, the reflectivity (i.e., the fraction of radiation reflected) is determined solely by the refractive index according to the relation.

$$\rho = \frac{I_r}{I_0} = \left(\frac{n-1}{n+1}\right)^2. \tag{4-4}$$

Thus, for instance, rock salt of index $n = 1.5$ has quite low reflectivity, $\rho = 0.043$. Germanium of a refractive index $n = 4.0$ reflects about 36 percent of the incident radiation; that is, $\rho = 0.36$.

If the angle of incidence ϕ is arbitrary rather than $0°$ (normal incidence), the reflectivity can be determined from *Fresnel's formulas.* These are written for *polarized radiation* in the following forms:

$$\rho_\perp = \sin^2(\phi - \chi)/\sin^2(\phi + \chi) \tag{4-5}$$

and

$$\rho_\parallel = \tan^2(\phi - \chi)/\tan^2(\phi + \chi). \tag{4-6}$$

Here $\rho_\perp$ is the reflectivity for the radiation polarized so that the electric vector of the wave is perpendicular to the plane of incidence; $\rho_\parallel$ refers to the wave with the electric vector parallel to the plane of incidence. χ denotes the angle of refraction determined by Snell's law (Eq. 4-1). Unpolarized radiation may be thought of as comprised of equal amounts of randomly mixed perpendicular and parallel components. The reflectivity for unpolarized radiation is then the average value obtained from Eqs. 4-5 and 4-6; that is, $\rho = \frac{1}{2}(\rho_\perp + \rho_\parallel)$.

The dependence of reflectivity on the angle of incidence is not obvious from Frensel's equations because of the implicit effect of Snell's law. However, several important features may be noted. First, we see that at normal incidence ($\phi = 0$) Eqs. 4-5 and 4-6 reduce to Eq. 4-4. Second, we observe that $\rho_\parallel$ becomes zero when $\phi + \chi = \pi/2$, since the denominator in Eq. 4-6 tends to infinity. Eliminating χ by using Eq. 4-1, we then obtain

$$\tan \phi_B = n. \tag{4-7}$$

The angle of incidence defined by this relation is called the *Brewster angle*. Radiation incident at this angle will have no parallel polarized component at all in the reflected beam ($\rho_\parallel = 0$), and consequently it will be fully polarized in the perpendicular direction. This circumstance is utilized to obtain polarized infrared radiation, which is otherwise impossible to attain by the conventional means. Windows inclined at the Brewster angle also permit passage of radiation (at least of the p-component) without any reflection loss—a remarkable advantage. Third, at large angles of incidence ($\phi \to \pi/2$) $\rho_\perp$, $\rho_\parallel$, and ρ tend to assume the maximum value of unity. This is obvious from the trigonometric relations and from the quadratic form of Eqs. 4-5 and 4-6. For the same reasons we obtain $\rho_\perp = \rho_\parallel = \rho = 1$ when $\chi = \pi/2$. This situation arises when radiation proceeds from the inside of the medium toward the boundary with the empty space. From Eq. 4-1 we obtain for this condition

$$\sin \phi_c = n. \tag{4-8}$$

The angle ϕ_c is called the critical angle. Radiation arriving at the boundary at this angle (or an angle $\phi > \phi_c$) from the inside of the medium is *totally reflected*. When the solid is not perfectly transparent, but has a measurable absorption, Fresnel's formulas become complex and in general rather unwieldy. However, the special case of normal incidence is still simple and noteworthy, namely,

$$\rho = \frac{(n - 1)^2 + k^2}{(n + 1)^2 + k^2}. \tag{4-9}$$

Here k is the extinction coefficient defined by Eq. 4-3. Equation 4-9 is more general than Eq. 4-4 as it shows that high reflectivity results not only when the refractive index is high, but also when k

is large. This is typically the case in metals; in transparent crystals it is nearly so in the middle of the dispersion band where k goes through a maximum.

The property of various crystals to reflect radiation in almost metallic fashion over a certain spectral range was first noted by E. F. Nichols, who was studying with Heinrich Rubens in Berlin (1897). When blackbody radiation was reflected several times from a crystal which had low reflectivity everywhere except in its dispersion region, only a narrow spectral band eventually remained; hence the name *residual rays* or, in German, *Reststrahlen*. Quartz was found to have two reststrahlen bands, one at 9μ and another at 21μ. A single reststrahlen band was found for calcite at 29μ, rock salt at 52μ, sylvite at 63μ, etc. Selective reflection by the reststrahlen method may be used to isolate narrow spectral bands from the infrared spectrum in the same way color filters are used in the visible.

Metallic Reflection. We shall now consider *reflectivity of metals* because of their importance for construction of reflecting optical components which are widely used in infrared instruments. Metals are characterized by their electrical conductivity, which, we know, is caused by the very high density of free electrons present in their structure. On classical theory the conduction electrons in a metal were considered to behave somewhat like molecules of a gas. Under the influence of the applied electromotive force, the electrons drift through the metal, making frequent collisions with the metal atoms. The greater the average time interval $(\bar{\tau})$ between collisons, the smaller the hindrance to electron motion and the higher the conductivity.

This classical theory yields an expression for the electrical conductivity σ_e of the metal

$$\sigma_e = N_e e^2 \bar{\tau}/m, \tag{4-10}$$

where N_e is the number of electrons per unit volume, e the electron charge, and m the mass of the electron. The inertial mass of conduction electrons is so small that they are free to respond to ac electromagnetic fields even at very high frequencies extending well beyond the microwaves into the infrared. Therefore, electrical conductivity determines the optical properties of metals in the infrared. The laws of refraction and reflection originally derived for insulating media are found to apply to metals, provided that the refractive index is formally replaced by a complex quantity, $n + ik$, k being the extinction coefficient already mentioned. The classical electron theory yields a relation between the complex refractive index and conductivity which can be written as:

$$(n + ik)^2 = 1 + 2i\sigma_e/\nu, \tag{4-11}$$

provided that $\nu < (\bar{\tau})^{-1}$. When $k \gg 1$, which is always the case with metals, we find that

$$n \approx k \approx (\sigma_e/\nu)^{1/2}. \tag{4-12}$$

Rearranging Eq. 4-9 and inserting into it from Eq. 4-12, we obtain

$$\rho = 1 - \frac{4n}{(n+1)^2 + k^2},$$

or

$$\rho \approx 1 - (2\nu/\sigma_e)^{1/2}. \tag{4-13}$$

This is the formula originally discovered in a semi-empirical way by Hagen and Rubens and later derived by P. Drude (1905) from classical electron theory of metals. In spite of the simple model assumed by the free-electron theory and the approximations made in the derivation of the formula, the results calculated from it come quite close to the observed values. Silver, for instance, has conductivity 0.67×10^{-6} ohm^{-1} cm^{-1}, or 6×10^{17} sec^{-1}, when expressed in electrostatic units, which are the proper kind to be used in Eq. 4-13. Therefore, at a frequency of 3×10^{13} sec^{-1} (corresponding to $\lambda = 10\mu$) silver should have reflectivity $\rho = 1 - (.0001)^{1/2} = 0.99$. The observed value for a freshly deposited silver coating is given as 98.9 percent. Silver is the best electrical conductor, and it is also the best reflector—as long as it is free of tarnish. Gold (which is nontarnishing) is an excellent reflector for infrared, and so is aluminum, which is often used as vacuum-deposited coatings on glass mirrors. Reflectivities of these and some other metals are given in Fig. 4-3.

Because the absorption in metals is very high, radiation penetrates only a very short distance into the metal (Eq. 4-2). In the present example of silver, at 10μ wavelength $k = 140$ (from Eq. 4-12) and

$\alpha = 1.8 \times 10^6$ cm^{-1} (from Eq. 4-3). From Eq. 4-2 we see that the intensity of radiation would become attenuated to e^{-1} (which is about 0.37, or 37 percent) in a depth $x = \alpha^{-1} = 5.6 \times 10^{-7}$ cm, or 56Å. Because of the small penetration depth, the constitution of the very surface of metal is most important. Surface of a metal polished by mechanical means (buffing) is highly disordered and thus has a conductivity lower than a pure, strain-free solid. Also, surfaces of most metals are subject to oxidation or corrosion when exposed to

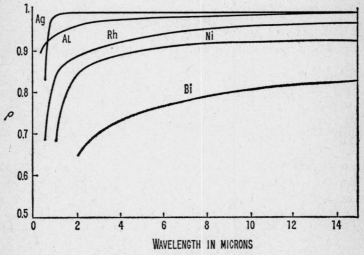

FIG. 4-3   Reflectivity of various metals in the infrared.

atmosphere, and it is the conductivity of the altered surface layer which determines the reflectivity. We shall not talk here about the effect of surface roughness on reflectivity of metals or insulators. Experimentalists tend to dismiss it as insignificant whenever they deal with radiation of wavelength longer than the average "wavelength" of the surface profile. This is a fairly good rule, but it applies only when the surface asperities are on a very fine scale compared with the wavelength. When the two are on about the same scale, scattering becomes significant and the specular reflectivity is impaired.

TABLE 4-1   *Infrared-Transmitting Materials*

Material	n (at $\lambda = 2\mu$)	Limit of Transmission (approx.)
Quartz, SiO_2	1.50	3μ
Sapphire, Al_2O_3	1.78	7
Irtran-1, (MgF_2)	1.4	8
Fluorite, CaF_2	1.45	9
Irtran-2, (ZnS)	2.28	14
Rock salt, NaCl	1.54	16
AgCl	2.01	24
KBr	1.65	25
KRS-5 (TlI-TlBr)	2.60	40
CsI	1.75	50
Optical Crown Glasses	1.5	2.8
Vitreous Silica	1.42	3.7
Special IR Glasses	1.75	5.5
As_2S_3-Glass	2.4	12
Silicon	3.4	40 *
Germanium	4.1	50 *

* NOTE: Various absorption bands may be present between 8 and 35μ, depending upon impurities present.

Optical Materials.   We shall add now only a few words about optical materials which are commonly used in construction of infrared optical instruments. The most important of these materials, arranged in the order of their long-wavelength transmission limit, are listed in Table 4-1. The transmission limits given in the table are

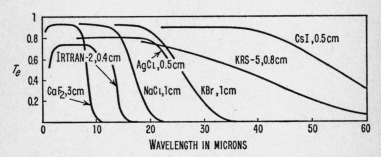

FIG. 4-4   Transmittance of various materials in the infrared.

actually not very sharp as may be seen in Fig. 4-4. The quantity plotted in the figure is the so-called *external transmittance*

$$T_e = (1 - \rho)^2 e^{-\alpha x}. \qquad (4\text{-}14)$$

The exponential term in this formula represents the absorptive attenuation according to the Lambert-Bouguer law (Eq. 4-2). The term $(1 - \rho)^2$ represents the loss by reflection, and it is squared because two reflections take place (front and back surface). It is well to keep in mind that transmittance is not a property of the material alone, but depends also on thickness.

Infrared transmitting materials to be used for a given purpose are chosen not only by their optical properties, but also by considerations regarding their chemical resistance, mechanical strength, temperature endurance, etc. For instance, rock salt is an excellent material usable to at least 16μ, but it is not very strong and is readily soluble in water. Therefore, it is unsuited for service in the open atmosphere. In its place one may consider sintered zinc sulfide (Irtran-2), which resists water quite well but does not transmit as far in the infrared and has greater absorption.

Various materials have their own individual weaknesses which must be considered for each particular application. Quartz has a very limited transmission beyond 3μ, rock salt is water soluble, silver chloride is exceedingly soft, KRS-5 is toxic, and cesium iodide is very expensive. Glasses have limited transmission in the infrared, except the arsenic trisulfide type, which, unfortunately, is toxic and poorly resistant to thermal shock. Semiconductors are opaque in the near infrared and have high reflection loss. Even though the choice of materials is actually greater than the selection shown in Table 4-1, one can seldom find a material perfectly suited for a given purpose, and the final choice is usually a matter of compromise.

All of the materials listed in Table 4-1 are inorganic solids. Organic glasses (polymers, plastics) find only limited use in the infrared, principally because they have numerous absorption bands in consequence of their molecular constitution. Furthermore, they are rather soft and do not stand up well at elevated temperatures. They are sometimes used in the form of thin films for cell windows and as protective coatings. Polyethylene is particularly useful because of its simple absorption spectrum; it has only three major absorption bands, at 3.5, 6.8, and 13.6μ. Beyond that it is quite transparent into the far infrared. Black polyethylene finds use as a filter to prevent the visible and near infrared from entering sensitive detectors for the far infrared radiation.

OPTICAL SYSTEMS

Lenses and Mirrors. The purpose of infrared optical systems is to form real images of objects. The objects may be emitting their own radiation, or they may be illuminated by radiation from other sources. Viewing or examining the image for the information it conveys represents one large group of applications of the infrared. Examples of such applications are infrared photography, or infrared surveillance. The other major group of applications is related to infrared spectroscopy. In both cases the function of the optical system is to form an undistorted, sharp image and to make it as intense as possible.

Glass lenses of the type commonly used in the visible range can be used only in the very near infrared. The lens design principles which have been developed to a high degree of sophistication can be applied equally well to infrared lenses. The infrared transmitting materials available at present to the lens designer offer sufficient variety of refractive indices and dispersions so that achromatized and otherwise corrected compound lenses can be constructed. However, all such lens systems have only a fairly narrow operating wavelength range. When the operating range has to be broad, extending to the middle and far infrared, lenses are replaced by concave mirrors. The focusing properties of metallic mirrors are completely independent of wavelength; we may say they are perfectly achromatic. This was recognized as early as the 17th century by Sir Isaac Newton, who wrote in his "Optics" (Book One, Part One):

Seeing therefore the Improvement of Telescopes of given lengths by Refractions is desperate; I contrived heretofore a Perspective by Reflexion, using instead of Object-glass a concave Metal. The diameter of the sphere to which the Metal was ground concave was about 25

English Inches and by consequence the length of the Instrument about six Inches and a quarter. . . . By comparing it with a pretty good Perspective of four Feet in length made with a concave Eye-glass, I could read at a greater distance with my own Instrument than with the Glass. Yet Objects appeared much darker in it than in the Glass, and partly because more Light was lost by Reflexion in the Metal, than by Refraction in the Glass, and partly because my Instrument was overcharged.

Concave mirrors for infrared optical systems are no longer made of metal. It is much better to grind and polish them from glass blanks and then coat the surface with aluminum or gold by evaporation *in vacuo*. Contrary to Newton's experience, it is then found that the efficiency of mirrors in the infrared greatly exceeds that of the lenses. Newton's mirrors had spherical surfaces because this was the figure which was easy to make by the common lens-grinding technique. *Spherical mirrors* are still frequently used when it does not matter that the wide-angle rays are not focused exactly to the same point as the near-axis rays (*spherical aberration*). In more exacting applications *aspherical* surfaces are required.

When an image of an infinitely distant point is to be formed, the appropriate reflecting surface is that of a *paraboloid* of revolution. For a point at a finite distance the correct shape is that of a concave *ellipsoid*. The object is placed in one of the foci, and the image is then formed in the other focus. A convex *hyperboloid* of revolution has a similar property except that one of its foci is virtual; hence an auxiliary concave mirror must be used with it (see Fig. 4-5).

All concave mirrors produce distorted images when the rays from the object arrive from directions deviating considerably from the axis of symmetry; the resulting aberrations are known as *astigmatism* and *coma*. In order to minimize these aberrations, the optical system should be designed so as to make the ray bundles impinge on the mirrors near normal incidence. If this is not possible and two or more mirrors are used in succession, the reflections should be arranged so that the off-axis aberrations tend to cancel out rather than to compound.

Diffraction Limit of Resolution. The requirements on "sharpness" of image are, in general, less stringent in infrared optical systems than in visible optics, with the possible exception of lenses for infrared photography. The reason is that the smallest resolvable area is limited by the size of the detector, which we have seen is seldom smaller than, say, 0.25 mm². In a reasonably well-designed system it is not difficult to form images of this size as far as the geometrical

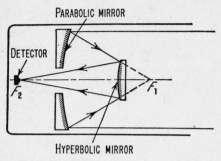

PARABOLIC MIRROR

DETECTOR

F_2

F_1

HYPERBOLIC MIRROR

FIG. 4-5   Cassegrain mirror optics of *f*-number N = 1.5.

optics is concerned. However, even in a perfectly designed and constructed optical system, a fundamental limit to the sharpness of the image is ultimately imposed by the wave properties of radiation. *Diffraction* of waves at the aperture of the system causes blurring of

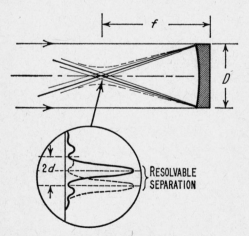

f

D

$2d$

RESOLVABLE SEPARATION

FIG. 4-6   Diffraction by a circular mirror.

the image which is more noticeable the greater the wavelength-to-aperture ratio. A typical situation is depicted in Fig. 4-6, which shows a perfect parabolic mirror forming an image of an infinitely distant point, say, a star. If we examine the image closely, we see that it consists of a bright central image surrounded by concentric rings gradually decreasing in intensity. Suppose our object is a double star of close spacing. In order that the images of the two stars be resolved they must be separated by at least the half-width of the central image. Lord Rayleigh introduced as a criterion of resolving power that separation of the two images at which the center of one falls on the first minimum of the other. For the effective width of the central image of a circular aperture he derived theoretically a formula

$$d = 1.22\lambda f/D = 1.22\lambda N, \qquad (4\text{-}14)$$

where $N = f/D$ is the *f-number* of the system, familiar to anyone who uses camera lenses. We can see, for instance, that a mirror of 10 cm diameter and 50 cm focal length ($N = 5$) would have at $\lambda = 10\mu$ a diffraction-limited resolution of about 60μ.

Image Brightness.   We shall now consider the factors determining the brightness of the image. This is very important because there never seems to be enough energy available to obtain useful signals even when the most sensitive detectors are used. The term *brightness* is borrowed from the terminology of visible photometry, and in the infrared it is more appropriate to use its equivalent, *radiance*. Let us introduce here the radiometric quantities as currently standardized in infrared terminology. The "strength" of a *point source* (e.g., a distant star) is described by its *radiant intensity*, J, measured in watts per unit of solid angle or steradian (w sr^{-1}). An extended source (e.g., the sun or a glowing tungsten filament) is characterized by its *radiant emittance*, W, measured in watts per unit area of surface (w cm^{-2}). The corresponding quantity when we refer to an image rather than a source is *irradiance*, W_i, likewise measured in w cm^{-2}. When the radiant power of the source varies with direction (recall, for example, Lambert's cosine law of blackbody emission), the appropriate characteristic quantity is *radiance*, I_0, defined as the radiant power emitted by unit area in a given direction per unit solid angle (w cm^{-2} sr^{-1}).

Consider now a simple optical system consisting of a concave mirror, a source, and its image (Fig. 4-7). The linear sizes of the image (a') and the source (a) and their distance from the mirror (f' and f, respectively) are in the proportion $a'/f' = a/f$; their areas ($A = a^2$, $A' = a'^2$) are in the proportion $A/A' = f^2/f'^2$. The solid angle into which each surface element of the source emits radiation is approximately (for $D/f \ll 1$) $\Omega = \pi D^2/4f^2$. The image receives radiation from the solid angle $\Omega' = \pi D^2/4f'^2$. The radiant power emitted by the source of radiance I_0 into the solid angle Ω is $I_0\Omega A$ (watts), and a fraction ρ thereof is reflected to the image, ρ denoting

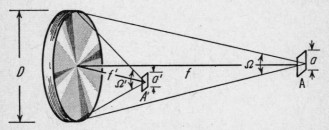

FIG. 4-7 Relation between source A and its image A' formed by a concave mirror of diameter D.

the reflectivity of the mirror. Hence the irradiance W'_i of the image is $W'_i = \rho I_0 \Omega A/A'$ (watts cm^{-2}). Substituting for Ω and A/A' from the expressions above, we obtain

$$W'_i = \pi I_0 \frac{\rho D^2}{4f'^2}. \tag{4-15}$$

Now πI_0 is the radiant power emitted by the source into a hemispherical solid angle, or its radiant emittance W. The ratio $(f'/D) = N'$ has the meaning of f-number introduced above. Hence we may write

$$W'_i = W \frac{\rho}{4N'^2}. \tag{4-16}$$

It is now apparent why in the photographic practice the inverse square of the f-number is called the *speed* of the lens: the irradiance of the image is proportional to it, and so it is possible to take shorter exposures with a lens of higher f-number. This terminology is often retained even with infrared systems. With an optical system of medium speed, say, $N = 5$, the irradiance of the image comes out to be only a small fraction (one percent) of the radiant emittance of the source, assuming $\rho = 1$. With a very "fast" mirror of f-number $N = 0.5$ we would obtain $W_i = W$, and it would seem that with mirrors of $N < 0.5$ we could actually exceed the emittance of the source. However, this is impossible. We must remember that Eqs. 4-15 and 4-16 have been derived under the assumption of $D/f \ll 1$, or $N \gg 1$, and therefore are certainly not applicable when $N < 1$. It can be shown rigorously that the irradiance of the image can never exceed the radiant emittance of the source. If this were possible the temperature of the image could exceed the temperature of the source, in violation of the second law of thermodynamics.

Even though the irradiance of the image remains less than the radiant emittance of the object, it is always advantageous to use an optical system of large aperture. Assume that the image of the source in Fig. 4-7 just covers the sensitive area of the receiver. If the same receiver of area A' were to be illuminated by the source A from a distance f directly (i.e., without any optical system), its irradiance would be $I_0 \Omega_0 A / A'$, where $\Omega_0 = A'/f^2$ is the solid angle intercepted by the receiver. With the use of the mirror, we have seen that the irradiance was $\rho I_0 \Omega A / A'$. Thus the increase gained by the use of mirrors amounts to a factor $\rho \Omega / \Omega_0$, which (for $\rho = 1$) is just equal to the ratio of the area of the mirror to the area of the receiver.

Some Optical Systems. Concave mirrors lend themselves well to the design of optical systems of high speed. Figure 4-5 shows an example of simple *Cassegrainian* system of f-number $N = 1.5$ of the type often used in infrared radiometers or target-tracking cameras. The parabolic mirror forms the image of a distant source at the focus F_1 that coincides with the virtual focus of the convex hyperbolic mirror, which then forms the real image in the focal point F_2.

An instructive example of appropriate use of various types of mirrors is seen in the optical system used in a common infrared prism spectrometer (Fig. 4-8). The source of radiation (globar rod) is imaged on the entrance slit of the spectrometer by a condensing mirror of $N = 3.5$. This condenser is a simple spherical mirror

since the quality of image obtained with it at near normal incidence
is better than required for the purpose, which is merely that the slit
be filled with radiation. The illuminated entrance slit is then imaged
to infinity by the so-called collimator; this has to be a parabolic
mirror. Here an off-axis mirror is used, meaning a section of a larger
parabolic mirror (shown in dashed lines in the figure) the axis of
which passes through the slit. The parallel bundle of rays formed by
the collimator is sent to the prism and back again after reflection on
a plane mirror placed behind it. The rays refracted by the prism

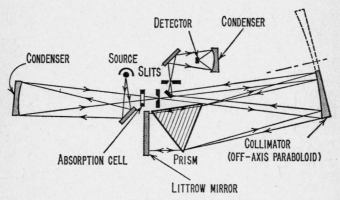

FIG. 4-8   Optical system of a prism spectrometer.

according to their wavelength and the dispersion properties of the
prism material (NaCl or KBr) arrive at the collimator still as a
parallel bundle, but at a slightly different angle. The collimator
focuses the parallel bundle upon the exit slit. If the radiation were
monochromatic, only one image of the entrance slit would be formed
on the exit slit. With blackbody radiation a broad band of images
(i.e., a continuous spectrum) is formed in the plane of the exit slit.
The desired wavelength is selected by slight turning of the plane
mirror behind the prism. With a rock salt prism about 5° is enough
to scan the spectrum from 5 to 15μ. The radiation emerging from
the exit slit is deflected by a 45° plane mirror onto an elliptical
mirror which focuses the radiation on the thermocouple receiver.

The foci of the ellipse coincide with the exit slit and the receiver of the thermocouple, respectively. Note that throughout the optical path in the spectrometer the focal distances and the sizes of the mirrors are chosen so that the entire radiation flux from the source is channeled economically and effectively to the detector. In order to obtain absorption spectra of gases or liquids, the sample is placed in a cell in front of the entrance slit. The instrument can also be used as a monochromator, to select a desired wavelength from a continuous spectrum. The particular arrangement shown in Fig. 4-8 represents a spectrograph of the *Littrow* type, named after O. von Littrow (1863), who thought of using the plane mirror to double the refraction of the prism.

REFERENCES

W. L. Wolfe and S. S. Ballard, "Optical Materials, Films and Filters for Infrared Instrumentation," Proc. Inst. Radio Eng. **47,** 1540 (1959).

F. A. Jenkins and H. E. White, *Fundamentals of Optics* (McGraw-Hill Book Company, New York, 1957).

SPECTROMETERS

Dispersion by a Prism.   Separation of infrared radiation into its spectral components can be accomplished by refraction, diffraction, or interference. We have just seen the optical system of a prism spectrometer. When a parallel beam of radiation passes through a prism, rays of different wavelengths are deviated to a varying degree depending on the refractive index (compare Fig. 4-1). If we follow the path of a ray through a prism of apical angle α (Fig. 4-9), we see that the deviation θ (i.e., the angle between the incident and refracted rays) is equal to $\phi_1 + \phi_2 - \alpha$ while the sum of the angles of refraction is $\chi_1 + \chi_2 = \alpha$. We want to know how much the deviation varies with wavelength, or in other words, what is the value of $d\theta/d\lambda$ (the *dispersion*) at any given wavelength. We shall first determine $d\theta/dn$ and then, knowing n as an empirical function of λ, we can obtain $d\theta/d\lambda$ as a product $(d\theta/dn) \times (dn/d\lambda)$.

When the ray passes through the prism symmetrically ($\phi_1 = \phi_2$

$= \phi$ and $\chi_1 = \chi_2 = \chi$—the position of *minimum deviation*), we see that $\phi = \frac{1}{2}(\theta + \alpha)$ and $\chi = \frac{1}{2}\alpha$. Inserting this into Snell's law (Eq. 4-1), we have $n = \sin \frac{1}{2}(\theta + \alpha)/\sin(\alpha/2)$, and after differentiation and some manipulation we obtain

$$\frac{d\theta}{dn} = 2 \sin(\alpha/2)/[1 - n^2 \sin^2(\alpha/2)]^{1/2}. \qquad (4\text{-}17)$$

Obviously, it is desirable to have $\sin(\alpha/2)$ and n large; however, their product must not exceed one, lest the denominator become zero. This condition puts a limit on the apical angle of a prism having a

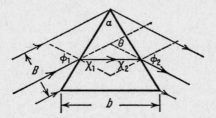

FIG. 4-9   Refraction through a prism.

given refractive index; with $n = 1.75$, α must be smaller than 69°. Prisms are most often made with a 60-degree angle. In this case Eq. 4-17 simplifies to

$$\frac{d\theta}{dn} = (1 - \tfrac{1}{4}n^2)^{-1/2}. \qquad (4\text{-}18)$$

Now, to get the dispersion we must multiply $d\theta/dn$ by $dn/d\lambda$, which is just the slope of the n-vs.-λ curve as shown, for instance, in Fig. 4-1. Apparently, $dn/d\lambda$ varies strongly with wavelength and so will the dispersion of the prism. Over the wavelength range in which various prism materials can be used, $dn/d\lambda$ is found to vary from about 0.002 to $0.02/\mu$. Rocksalt at $\lambda = 10\mu$ has $dn/d\lambda = 0.0073/\mu$; its refractive index is 1.49 at this wavelength. Thus for a 60-degree prism we obtain, by Eq. 4-18, $d\theta/dn = 1.50$ radians and $d\theta/d\lambda = 1.50 \times 0.0073 = 0.011$ radian$/\mu$. With a mirror of focal distance $f = 50$ cm the image of the entrance slit will deviate by about 0.55 cm for two wavelengths one micron apart.

In general, the separation of the two images will be

$$\Delta x = f \frac{d\theta}{d\lambda} \Delta\lambda.$$

The smallest wavelength interval $\Delta\lambda_e$ we would expect to resolve with a given combination of prism and mirror is determined by the condition that Δx is equal to the slit width s; hence

$$\Delta\lambda_e = \frac{s}{f} \frac{d\lambda}{d\theta}. \qquad (4\text{-}20)$$

It would seem possible to resolve very closely spaced spectral lines by merely making the slit as narrow as the sensitivity of the detector allows. When this condition applies, we say that the resolution is *energy-limited*. However, even if we had all the energy needed to obtain a useful signal with the narrowest slits we could not attain arbitrarily high resolution; the reason is *diffraction*. Just as we have seen that the image of a point source becomes broadened when formed by a mirror of finite size (Eq. 4-14), so it can be shown that the image of a slit has an effective angular width $\Delta\theta = \lambda/B$, where B denotes the breadth of the beam passing through the prism (Fig. 4-9). From this expression we obtain for the smallest resolvable wavelength difference

$$\Delta\lambda_d = \frac{\lambda}{B} \frac{d\lambda}{d\theta}. \qquad (4\text{-}21)$$

This is the resolution under *diffraction-limited* conditions. Since, at a given wavelength, $d\lambda/d\theta$ is determined by the prism material, the only thing we can do in order to keep $\Delta\lambda_d$ small is to make B large. This is why it is good to use a large prism. With a mirror of a focal distance $f = 50$ cm, slit width $s = 0.01$ cm, and dispersion $d\theta/d\lambda = 0.011$ radian/μ (at 10μ), our rocksalt prism would have energy-limited resolution of 0.018μ; with the Littrow mirror it would become 0.009μ because of the double passage through the prism. The diffraction-limited resolution depends on the size of the prism. With a $60°$ prism having 7-cm sides, the useful beamwidth is about $B = 4$ cm. Then the diffraction-limited resolution at 10μ is 0.027μ, and it would become even greater at longer wavelengths. Spectral resolution is often quoted in terms of wavenumber rather than wavelength differences. Differentiating Eq. 1-1 we obtain for conversion from $\Delta\lambda$ to $\Delta\nu'$ an expression $|\Delta\nu'| = \Delta\lambda/\lambda^2$; thus the figure of $\Delta\lambda = 0.01\mu$ at 10μ corresponds to a wavenumber difference 1.0 cm^{-1}; this is a pretty good figure for a typical prism spectrometer. An often-used measure of performance of a prism is its *resolving power*, defined as the dimensionless ratio $\lambda/\Delta\lambda$.

Dispersion by a Grating. We shall now talk about the *diffraction grating* as a dispersive element of the spectrometer. Although first diffraction gratings were made at the time of Herschel's investigations (notably by J. von Fraunhofer in Munich), their introduction to infrared spectroscopy had to wait more than half a century. By that time H. A. Rowland had greatly perfected the art of mechanically ruling gratings and had delivered a specially made concave grating of 3610 lines/inch to S. P. Langley for his work on the solar spectrum. Later R. W. Wood, who succeeded Rowland at Johns Hopkins University, developed the technique for concentrating the intensity of diffracted light into the desired direction by control of the groove shape (*echelette* grating). Coarse-grooved echelettes had been introduced into infrared spectroscopy by H. M. Randall in the late thirties, and the advantages of gratings became rapidly recognized. Today their use is almost as widespread as that of prisms.

A diffraction grating for the infrared consists of an optically flat glass blank coated with aluminum or gold film into which is ruled a great number of accurately parallel and equidistant grooves. Their density may range from a few hundred to a few thousand lines per inch depending on the spectral range to be covered. In an "ordinary" grating (Fig. 4-10a) the grooves act more or less as scattering obstacles on the otherwise continuous mirror. Consider two parallel rays *1*, *2* incident normally at two points *A*, *A'* exactly one spacing *S* apart. Of all the rays radiating from points *A* and *A'* two parallel rays *1'*, *2'*, will be inclined at an angle θ such that the distance *AB* will be an integral multiple *m* of the wavelength λ. Then the wave vibrations in the rays *1'* and *2'* will be in phase, and the radiation intensity will be reinforced in that particular direction. This condition can be written as

$$S \sin \theta = m\lambda,$$

or, for arbitrary angle of incidence θ_i,

$$S(\sin \theta_i + \sin \theta) = m\lambda. \tag{4-22}$$

For $m = 0$ we obtain specular reflection; $m = 1, 2, 3 \ldots$ give diffractions of first, second, third . . . *order* which deviate more and more from the specularly reflected ray. Obviously, θ cannot exceed 90°, and so the spacing must satisfy condition $S \geq \lambda m$. In practice the maximum diffraction angle is kept below 60°, and thus $S \geq 1.15\lambda m$.

When monochromatic radiation illuminates a grating of the type shown in Fig. 4-10a, radiation will be thrown into sharply defined directions $\pm\theta_1, \pm\theta_2, \pm\theta_3 \ldots$, the first order being the strongest and

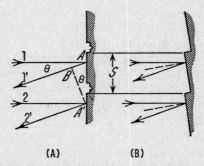

(A)   (B)

FIG. 4-10   Diffraction by an ordinary grating (a), and by an echelette grating (b).

the higher orders becoming progressively weaker. R. W. Wood's contribution was to show that by slanting the reflecting portions of the grooves so that they reflect specularly it is possible to concentrate almost all of the diffracted energy in one selected order. The grating is then said to be blazed for the particular diffraction order and wavelength. The groove profile best suited for this purpose is shown in Fig. 4-10b. In recent years, largely through the efforts of G. R. Harrison of M.I.T., it has become possible to manufacture echelette gratings of excellent quality and of resolving power greater than that of prisms of comparable size and cost. Unlike Rowland's concave gratings, echelettes are usually plane, and therefore they require optical imaging systems similar to those used with prisms. For instance, in the arrangement shown in Fig. 4-8 the prism may simply be taken out, and the Littrow mirror be replaced by the grating, having made adjustment for the direction of the selected diffraction order. An arrangement often used with gratings spectrographs is the so-called *Ebert mounting* shown in Fig. 4-11.

The dispersion of grating is found by differentiating Eq. 4-22:

$$\frac{d\theta}{d\lambda} = \frac{m}{S \cos \theta}. \tag{4-23}$$

There are no empirical constants in this formula, and the dispersion is a simple function of two exactly measurable quantities S and θ.

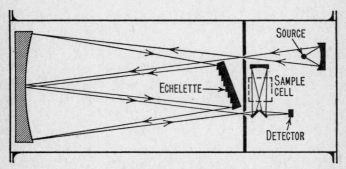

FIG. 4-11 Grating spectrometer of the Ebert type; vacuum enclosure is provided for work in far infrared.

This fact was of great significance in the early days of infrared spectroscopy. Until gratings suitable for the infrared became available, the wavelengths of thermal radiation could not be determined with any degree of confidence because the semi-empirical dispersion curves of prism materials were known only over the visible range. As these curves were extrapolated into the infrared, the wavelength scale became more and more uncertain as one went farther away in the long-wave region. This uncertainty was resolved when the dispersion curves of prisms were determined in terms of absolute wavelength scale established by means of diffraction gratings. As long as good gratings were a rarity, their use was very limited, and most of the work in spectroscopy was done with prisms. Echelette gratings are now finding increasing use in infrared spectrometers.

The resolution of spectral lines obtainable with a grating is determined by the same factors as with the prism. In the energy-limited case we obtain from Eqs. 4-20 and 4-23

$$\Delta\lambda_e = \frac{s}{f} \frac{S \cos \theta}{m}. \qquad (4\text{-}24)$$

In the diffraction-limited case one obtains a formula identical with Eq. 4-21. The resolving power of a grating is found to be $(\lambda/\Delta\lambda)$ $= mN$, where N is the total number of lines in the ruled surface.

The main advantage of gratings is found in the region from 2.5 to 5μ where they offer the superior resolution that is required in molecular spectroscopy. Blazed gratings also seem to be more efficient than prisms and thus deliver more energy to the detector under the same conditions. Their disadvantage is the overlapping of higher-order spectra.

We can see from Eq. 4-22 that radiation of wavelength λ will be diffracted by the same angle θ in the first order as radiation of wavelength $\lambda/2$ in the second order, etc. To avoid possible confusion resulting from these coincidences, it is necessary to select the desired spectral range with a foreprism or a filter. In order to cover a wide range of wavelengths the same grating may be used in several successive orders. Thus an echelette grating having 2500 lines per inch may be used in the first order for the wavelength range from 15 to 5μ, in the second order from 5 to 3.5μ, in the third order from 3.75 to 2.5μ, and in the fourth order from 2.5 to 2μ. Orders higher than fourth are almost never used because the separation of possible overlaps becomes difficult. In some spectrographs the difficulty is overcome by using two gratings of different spacings, each only in the first two orders.

Practical Spectrometers.   Modern spectrometers of both the prism type and the grating type include a number of accessories which make the life of the practicing spectroscopist much easier than it was in the early days of infrared spectroscopy. When Coblentz started

(1903) on his pioneering investigation of infrared spectra in the basement of the physics laboratory at Cornell University, it took him about four hours to record one spectrum, and this he had to do by setting the prism for each wavelength, reading the corresponding deflections of the radiometer by telescope, and plotting the spectrum point by point on graph paper. Nowadays, most spectrometers automatically record the transmittance as the spectrum is continually scanned. Mechanical drive of adjustable speed turns the Littrow mirror or the grating through a cam-and-lever linkage so as to make the scale linear in wavelength or wavenumber; slit widths are adjusted at the same time so that the energy level remains constant through the spectrum; gratings and filters are automatically changed over at predetermined wavelength; and the result is traced as a neat curve on a chart with preprinted wavelength and transmittance scales. All that remains to be done is to place the sample in the beam and push the start button; the machine even stops itself.

Instruments most useful for routine analytical work are of the so-called *double-beam* type. In these instruments the radiation from the source is split into two beams, one of which receives the sample cell. The other beam serves as a reference. The radiation from the two beams is alternately passed through the spectrometer of a conventional type. A synchronously operated switch passes the amplified signal from the detector through two demodulators which generate dc signals proportional to the energy in the sample path and reference path, respectively. The difference of the two signals is made to operate a servomotor which inserts an attenuator in the reference path so that the radiation fluxes in the two paths are equalized. Coupled with the motion of the attenuator is a recording pen which moves across the width of the chart while the chart is being pulled along by the motor that drives the spectrometer wavelength control. If logarithmic instead of linear amplifiers are used, the difference signal can be used to produce a recording of the ratio of the two signals. Use of two identical paths in the double-beam instruments eliminates the effect of absorption by atmospheric water and carbon dioxide whose bands are superimposed on the spectrum of the sample in single-beam instruments. Likewise, when working with solutions, the absorption bands of the solvent can be eliminated by placing the pure solvent in the reference path.

Interferometers. We shall now say a few words about interferometers which are becoming increasingly important in infrared spectroscopy. The *Fabry-Perot interferometer* consists of two accurately parallel, transparent plates provided with partially transmitting and highly reflecting coatings of the inner surfaces. A bundle of parallel rays incident upon the front plate at an angle θ (Fig. 4-12) will be

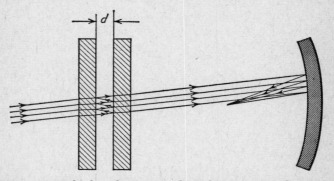

FIG. 4-12   Multiple reflections in the Fabry-Perot interferometer.

refracted, multiply-reflected between the plates, and refracted out again before being collected in the focal plane of a concave mirror. The waves in the rays emerging from the back plate have different phases depending on the path difference they traveled between the plates. As in the grating equation (4-22), we find that reinforcement (constructive interference) occurs when

$$2d \cos \theta = m\lambda. \qquad (4\text{-}26)$$

The order number m is equal to the number of reflections between the plates. Depending on the reflection loss at the coated surfaces, m may assume very high integral values. Consequently, angular dispersion and resolving power of interferometers can be much higher than that of prisms or gratings. The Fabry-Perot interferometer requires no entrance slit, and the circular exit aperture at the center of the interference pattern may be fairly large without substantial loss of resolutions. For this reason the Fabry-Perot interferometer is ideally suited for the construction of a fast-scanning spectrometer. The scanning of the desired wavelength range is effected by moving the plates to and fro. The disadvantages of the interferometer result from the necessity for using filters for separation of overlapping orders and from absorption in the interferometer plates and reflecting coatings.

REFERENCES

G. R. Harrison, R. C. Lord, and J. Loofbourow, *Practical Spectroscopy,* (Prentice-Hall, Englewood Cliffs, 1962).

G. R. Harrison, "The Production of Diffraction Gratings, I," J. Opt. Soc. Am. **39,** 413, 1949.

D. W. Robinson, "Ebert Spectrometer for the Far Infrared," J. Opt. Soc. Am. **49,** 966, 1959.

R. W. Terhune and C. W. Peters, "Rapid-Scan Spectroscopy with a Fabry-Perot Interferometer," J. Opt. Soc. Am. **51,** 530, 1961.

R. A. Waldron, *Waves and Oscillations* (Momentum Book #4, D. Van Nostrand Company, Princeton, N.J., 1964).

5   *Spectroscopy*

ORIGIN OF INFRARED SPECTRA

The first infrared spectrum was obtained in 1840 by Sir John F. W. Herschel, son of the discoverer of the infrared. By an ingenious method of evaporating alcohol from blackened paper (evaporography), he obtained a record of the near-infrared part of the solar spectrum and showed that it consisted of at least three disconnected regions. Some forty years later Langley published his excellent solar spectra (Fig. 2-3) and showed that there were absorption bands superimposed on the solar continuum. Through the work of F. Paschen, E. Aschkinass, and other investigators in the 1890s these bands were identified with those of water vapor and carbon dioxide. When K. J. Ångström demonstrated that the absorption bands of different gases consisting of the same atoms (e.g., CO and CO_2) have different infrared absorption spectra, it became evident that infrared spectra are related to molecular rather than atomic properties.

The evidence was further strengthened by investigations on organic compounds (consisting mainly of C and H atoms). The pioneers of infrared spectroscopy in the field of organic chemistry were W. de W. Abney and E. R. Festing, who used photographic plates specially sensitized to wavelengths up to 1.3μ. Unfortunately, in this region they could observe only the overtone and combination frequencies of the fundamental C—H vibrations which lie beyond 2.7μ. This limitation was overcome by W. H. Julius, who extended the spectra to about 10μ by the use of the rocksalt prism and the bolometer. The most extensive study of infrared spectra of organic compounds in this period was made by W. W. Coblentz, whose work paved the way for the emergence of structural *molecular spectroscopy*. The latter was then developed in the 1920s by the efforts of J. Lecomte and others.

The characteristic of infrared spectroscopy which makes it invaluable to the organic chemist is its ability to identify certain *molecular groups* in compounds. These include, in particular, the following groups: C—C (alkane), C=C (alkene) and C=C (aromatic), C≡C, C—H (in various configurations), C=O, C≡N, O—H, N=H₂, and many others. Where elemental analysis or atomic spectroscopy would merely indicate the presence of the same elements, such as C, H, O, and N, infrared spectroscopy provides definite clues as to the molecular structure of the compound. This is made possible by the fact that the energy of the infrared quanta is so low that it does not cause electronic excitations in the constituent atoms, but it suffices to excite vibrations and rotations of atoms or groups of atoms as a whole.

Infrared spectra can be observed in all three states of matter: gaseous, liquid, and solid. In gases the molecules have enough room to vibrate and rotate at the same time, thus giving rise to complex vibration-rotation bands. In liquids the molecules can still vibrate quite freely, but their rotations are restrained; their spectra are, consequently, somewhat simplified. In solids the constraints are tightened, but in the molecular crystals, which are only weakly bonded, the vibrations of characteristic groups are still present. In more strongly bonded crystals (e.g., ionic crystals) the vibrations can take place only when the whole crystal lattice vibrates. This gives rise to strong dispersion bands, which we have already encountered in Chapter 4. The method best suited for observing the spectra of gases and liquids is absorption. The absorption in solids is often so strong that it is necessary to use them in the form of fine particles mixed with a transparent diluent (KBr or polyethylene powder); or one can obtain the spectra of strongly absorbing solids by reflection. Emission is almost never used in infrared spectroscopy of organic compounds since the high temperatures required would tend to destroy the groups under study. Gases can be studied, of course, by emission in the infrared (e.g., in flames and electric discharges). Spectral emission from incandescent inorganic solids may likewise be used to investigate their thermal properties.

VIBRATION OF DIATOMIC MOLECULES

Infrared absorption is observed only in gases which consist of *polar molecules*, such as HCl, CO, H_2O or NH_3. Covalently bonded molecules such as H_2, O_2 or N_2 do not cause absorption in the infrared. Consider a diatomic molecule consisting of two ions of opposite charge—for example, H^+Cl^-, shown in Fig. 5-1. The two charges are attracted to each other by a *Coulomb force* (F) and held apart by a repulsive force resulting from the interaction of electrons as the ion cores approach one another. As a result of the two forces, the atoms assume a well-defined equilibrium distance, typically a few Å apart. Now if such a molecular *dipole* is exposed to the alternating electric field of an electromagnetic wave, it is subject to a

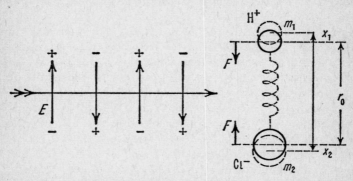

FIG. 5-1   Spring-and-mass model of a diatomic, polar molecule of HCl. The electric vector of a wave coming from the left is shown by alternating arrows.

periodic force. The two masses then vibrate about the equilibrium position as if they were connected by an elastic spring.

This is a classical description of a dipolar molecular vibrator. On this model the frequency of vibration is

$$\nu = \frac{1}{2\pi} (k/m)^{1/2}, \tag{5-1}$$

where k is the restoring force, $k = -F/x$, and $m = (m_1 + m_2)/m_1 m_2$ is the so-called *reduced mass*. In this way we replace the diatomic molecule by a single oscillator of mass m and displacement $x = x_1 + x_2$. Solution of the equation of motion of the mass m bound to the equilibrium point by a force proportional and opposite to the displacement ($F = -kx$) gives

$$x = A \cos 2\pi\nu t, \tag{5-2}$$

which describes harmonic motion of frequency ν and amplitude A. In actual molecules the force may not be strictly proportional to the displacement, particularly when the amplitude is large. In that case the vibration would have, in addition to the *fundamental frequency ν*, *overtone frequencies* 2ν, 3ν, ...

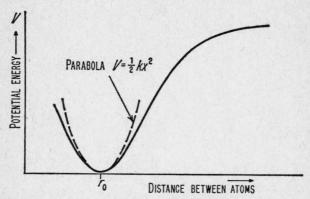

FIG. 5-2 Potential energy curve of a diatomic molecule; r_o is the equilibrium distance.

The potential energy of the oscillator is obtained from Eq. 5-2 by integrating the work done by the force $-kx$ over the distance from 0 to x, which yields $\frac{1}{2}kx^2$, or

$$V = 2\pi^2\nu^2A^2m \cos^2 2\pi\nu t.$$

The potential energy increases quadratically with displacement or, in other words, the potential curve is a parabola. In reality again, the potential curve in a diatomic molecule has a parabolic shape only near the equilibrium position; otherwise it has a course roughly as shown in Fig. 5-2.

We can readily write the expression for the kinetic energy $U = \frac{1}{2}mu^2$ of the oscillator by obtaining $u = dx/dt$ from Eq. 5-2,

$$U = 2\pi^2\nu^2A^2m \sin^2 2\pi\nu t.$$

The total energy E of the oscillator is then

$$E = U + V = 2\pi^2 v^2 m A^2. \tag{5-3}$$

In classical mechanics the energy of the oscillator could have any arbitrary value of energy, depending on the value of the amplitude A. However, when dealing with atomic particles we cannot use the laws of classical mechanics, and we already know that the energy they can possess is variable only in quantized increments of hv.

The appropriate description of atomic phenomena is provided by *wave mechanics*. The *Schrödinger equation* of a simple linear oscillator has a form

$$\frac{d^2\psi}{dx^2} + \frac{8\pi^2 m}{h^2}(E - 2\pi^2 v^2 m x^2)\psi = 0, \tag{5-4}$$

in which the square of the amplitude $|\psi|^2$ of the wave scalar ψ may be interpreted as the probability of finding the particle at a given position. Equation 5-4 can be simplified by substituting

$$\frac{2E}{hv} = \epsilon \quad \text{and} \quad \frac{4\pi^2 m v}{h}x^2 = y^2.$$

The equation

$$\frac{d^2\psi}{dy^2} + (\epsilon - y^2) = 0 \tag{5-5}$$

can be shown to have finite, single-valued solutions only for values of ϵ which are of the form $2v + 1$, $v = 0, 1, 2, 3 \ldots$ being a positive integer. (These are the eigenvalues of Eq. 5-5.) Physically meaningful solutions are, therefore, obtained when $2E/hv = 2v + 1$, or

$$E = (v + \tfrac{1}{2})hv. \tag{5-6}$$

Here v is the *vibration quantum number* of a diatomic molecule.

The vibrating molecule can absorb and emit radiation only by increments of $\Delta v = \pm 1$. This is the *selection rule* for vibrational transitions. For instance, from the lowest state ($v = 0$) in which it has energy $E_0 = \tfrac{1}{2}hv$ it can be excited to the state $v = 1$ of energy $E_1 = 1\tfrac{1}{2}hv$ by absorbing a quantum of energy $E_1 - E_0 = hv$ from the incident electromagnetic wave. Obviously, the frequency of vibration must be equal to that of the wave. If transitions $\Delta v = \pm 2$, etc., were permitted, the two frequencies would not be the same, in violation of Bohr's *correspondence principle*, which demands that the laws of classical mechanics and quantum mechanics be in agreement in the limit of large systems.

The residual energy $E_0 = \frac{1}{2}h\nu$, which the molecule has even when the two atoms are at the equilibrium distance and under no thermal excitation, is called *zero point energy* because it is retained even at $T = 0°K$.

Rotation of Diatomic Molecules. When the vibration bands of diatomic molecules in gases were first examined with spectrometers of low resolution, they consistently showed a double-humped ap-

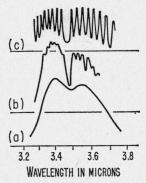

WAVELENGTH IN MICRONS

Fig. 5-3 The vibration-rotation band of HCl recorded with spectrometers of improved resolution; (a) CaF$_2$ prism (Burmeister, 1913); (b) Quartz prism (von Bahr, 1913); (c) grating (Imes, 1919).

pearance (Fig. 5-3a). As the spectroscopic technique improved, a rather striking fine structure of the humps emerged (Fig. 5-3b, c) and eventually became recognized as a result of molecular rotation. That the molecules rotate has long been postulated in the kinetic theory in order to account for the excess specific heat of gases consisting of polyatomic molecules. Here then was a visible effect of the conjectural rotation and, as it turned out, a beautiful example of quantization of rotational energy.

In a simple-minded way we may picture the diatomic molecule as a tiny dumbbell rotating about an axis perpendicular to the handle, which we shall assume to be perfectly rigid. The moment of inertia of the molecule is $I = mr_0^2$, m being the reduced mass of the two atoms and r_0 their distance. When rotating with angular velocity ω_r, the molecule has kinetic energy which, calculated classically, would be $E_r = \frac{1}{2}I\omega_r^2$. Consequently, the rotational energy could have any arbitrary value, depending on the magnitude of ω_r. If we write the Schrödinger wave equation for the molecular rotator and find its eigenvalues, we find that the kinetic energy of a rotating molecule can only have certain discrete values. These are given by

$$E_r = \frac{h^2}{8\pi^2 I} J(J + 1), \tag{5-7}$$

in which $J = 0, \pm 1, \pm 2, \ldots$ is the *rotational quantum number*. There is no zero-point rotational energy. The molecule can accept or give up rotational energy only by increments of $\Delta E_r = h\nu_r$, corresponding to changes of J by $+1$ or -1. The *selection rule* for rotational transitions is $\Delta J = 0$ or $\Delta J = \pm 1$. The actual frequency of rotation in the lowest quantum state $(J = 1)$ is obtained from Eq. 5-7 as $\nu_r = h/4\pi^2 I$. It turns out to be so low that it is not directly observable in the infrared. Pure rotational spectra of diatomic gases are observed in the microwave range. (For HCl the fundamental rotation corresponds to a wavelength of 0.945 millimeters.)

The complex bands, such as those shown in Fig. 5-3, are examples of the *vibration-rotation bands* typically observed in gases. The molecules vibrate as they rotate, and the two motions couple together in a way similar to that of two connected pendulums. In this case we know that *beats* will arise and their frequencies will be $\nu_{vib} \pm \nu_r$. Since ν_r is much smaller than ν_{vib}, the fundamental vibration frequency will be accompanied by a number of closely spaced rotational lines on either side of the center of the band. In quantum mechanical form the situation will be described by the expression for the vibrational-rotational energy of the molecule,

$$E_{vr} = (v + \tfrac{1}{2})h\nu + \frac{h^2}{8\pi^2 I} J(J + 1), \tag{5-8}$$

which follows from Eqs. 5-6 and 5-7. A transition between two energy levels $E_2 - E_1 = \Delta E_{vr}$ results from a simultaneous change in the vibrational and rotational energy,

$$E_{vr} = (v_2 - v_1)h\nu + \frac{h^2}{8\pi^2 I} [J_2(J_2 + 1) - J_1(J_1 + 1)].$$

For the fundamental band $v_2 - v_1 = 1$, and since $J_2 = J_1 \pm 1$, the equation can be rewritten as

$$\Delta E_{vr} = h\nu + \frac{h^2}{4\pi^2 I} J_1, \tag{5-9}$$

where $J_1 = \pm 1, 2, 3, \ldots$.

Investigation of rotation and vibration-rotation spectra made it possible to determine directly the interatomic distances in diatomic molecules. Having determined E_r or ΔE_{vr} from the observed spectra, we may solve Eq. 5-7 or 5-9 for the moment of inertia $I = mr_0^2$ and from it, knowing the atomic masses m_1 and m_2, we may calculate r_0. In our example of the HCl molecule r_0 is found to be 1.27Å. Distances of the same order of magnitude are found also in other diatomic molecules.

Polyatomic Molecules. Molecules consisting of more than two atoms have, in general, quite complicated spectra. A molecule containing N atoms can perform $3N$ kinds of motions. Three of them are simple translations which are irrelevant to the spectra, and three are rotations about the three principal axes of inertia. Thus there are $3N$-6 vibrations left, each of a different frequency. In *linear* molecules only rotations about the two axes perpendicular to the axis of the molecule contribute significantly to the rotational energy. Energy of rotation about the axis of the molecule is negligible. Consequently, linear molecules have only two rotational degrees of freedom and hence $3N$-5 independent vibrations. We can imagine that a molecule consisting of a number of atoms bound together with quasi-elastic forces would perform, when disturbed, a very complicated vibration. However, even a most complicated motion of this kind can be resolved into a set of $3N$-6 *normal vibrations* each of which is simple in the sense that all atoms in the molecule vibrate with one and the same frequency and maintain constant phase relationships. Moreover, individual normal vibrations are independent of each other, that is, they can be excited one at a time without coupling with any other.

Let us look at the normal modes of some of the simpler polyatomic molecules. A nonlinear, triatomic molecule such as H_2O has $(3 \times 3) - 6 = 3$ normal modes, as shown in Fig. 5-4. A linear, triatomic molecule such as CO_2 has $(3 \times 3) - 5 = 4$ normal modes, as shown in Fig. 5-5. Two of the modes are of the same type, differing only in the direction of vibration, and they have the same frequency. This is called *degeneracy*. In the molecule of methane, CH_4, which

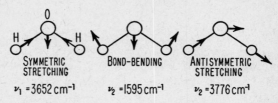

SYMMETRIC STRETCHING
$\nu_1 = 3652\ cm^{-1}$

BOND-BENDING
$\nu_2 = 1595\ cm^{-1}$

ANTISYMMETRIC STRETCHING
$\nu_2 = 3776\ cm^{-1}$

FIG. 5-4 **The three fundamental normal vibrations of a nonlinear molecule of H_2O.**

has $(5 \times 3) - 6 = 9$ normal modes of vibration, it is found that there are only four different fundamental frequencies; two vibrations are triply degenerate, one is doubly degenerate, and one is non-degenerate. Degeneracies result from symmetries of the molecules, and exact rules exist for their determination.

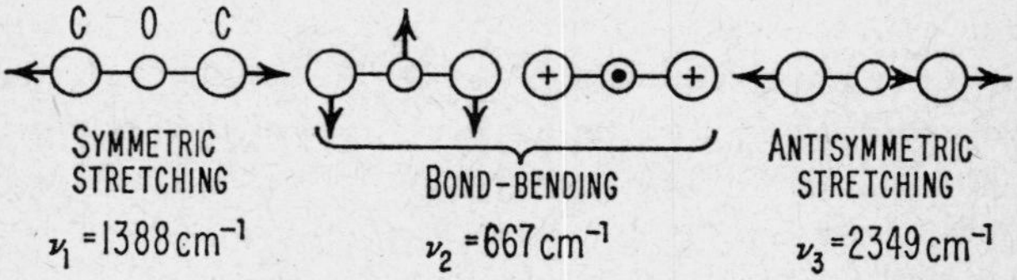

SYMMETRIC STRETCHING
$\nu_1 = 1388\ cm^{-1}$

BOND-BENDING
$\nu_2 = 667\ cm^{-1}$

ANTISYMMETRIC STRETCHING
$\nu_3 = 2349\ cm^{-1}$

FIG. 5-5 **Normal vibrations of a linear molecule of CO_2; the bond-bending vibration is doubly-degenerate.**

Rotations add to the complexity of spectra of polyatomic molecules. In diatomic molecules, which possessed only one moment of inertia, we could characterize the rotational energy level by one quantum number J. Polyatomic molecules have, in general, three different moments of inertia. If two of them are identical so that the molecule has only two principal moments, it is called a *symmetric top molecule* (e.g., CH_3Cl or CH_3CN). In this case Eq. 5-7 is modified by an additive term containing a second rotational quantum number

K. Molecules with three different moments of inertia are called *asymmetric tops;* in this category belong, for example, H_2O, CH_3OH, and all molecules of low symmetry. In asymmetric tops the rotational energy levels cannot be expressed by equations of the type shown in Eq. 5-7, and each molecule must be treated as a special case. Complete analysis of the vibration-rotation spectra of asymmetric top molecules belongs among the most difficult problems of theoretical molecular spectroscopy.

MOLECULAR SPECTROSCOPY

Even though the exact description of vibrational modes of a complex molecule may be impossible, certain types of vibrations may be recognized as typically associated with certain molecular groupings. This gives valuable clues to a possible determination of unknown molecular structures in chemical compounds. This type of spectral analysis has been extensively cultivated, in particular by organic chemists, and comprehensive *correlation charts* have been compiled. One of the best-known charts of this sort was published by N. B. Colthup in 1950; more extensive correlation tables have become available since and are to be found in references on molecular spectroscopy. A brief listing of characteristic vibrations observed in molecular groups often encountered in organic compounds is given in Table 5-1. Similar tables exist for inorganic compounds. The apparent large spread of the bands listed in

TABLE 5-1 *Characteristic Vibrations of Molecular Groups*

Group	Type	Wavenumber	Wavelength
H—O and H—N	Stretching	3700–3000 cm^{-1}	2.70–3.33μ
C—H	Stretching	3300–2700	3.0–3.7
C=O	Stretching	1850–1650	5.4–6.1
C≡C and C≡N	Stretching	1700–1580	5.9–6.3
H—N	Bending	1650–1490	6.1–6.7
C—H	Bending	1470–1300	6.8–7.7
O—H	Bending	1450–1200	6.9–8.3
C—O and C—N	Stretching	1300–900	7.7–11.1
C—C	Stretching	1200–800	6.9–12.5
C—H	Rocking	900–600	11.1–16.7

Table 5-1 is due in part to the omission of finer subdivisions which are actually quite useful. Thus, for instance, the C—H stretching vibration in hydrocarbons occurs at about 3300 cm^{-1} in alkynes (compounds with C≡C bonds), around 3000 cm^{-1} in alkenes (C=C bonds), and around 2900 cm in alkanes (C—C bonds); in aromatic (benzene ring) hydrocarbons it occurs between 3000 and 3100 cm^{-1}. Simultaneous observation of the C—H bending and C—C stretching vibrations at longer wavelengths makes possible still closer characterization of the molecule as to the type of substitution and the nature of substituting atoms or groups.

Quite apart from its value for determination of molecular structure, infrared spectroscopy is widely used for analysis, mainly of organic compounds. Since each compound has a unique infrared absorption spectrum, it can be identified by it as if by a fingerprint. (See Figs. 5-6 and 5-7.) For this purpose spectra of thousands of compounds have been recorded under standardized conditions and catalogued in such a way as to facilitate comparison. The most important catalogs of infrared spectra are the API (American Petroleum Institute) Project 44 (concerned mostly with hydrocarbons), the Sadtler catalog, containing almost 20,000 spectra of pure compounds and commercial products, and the DMS (Documentation of Molecular Spectroscopy) catalog, comprising over 7500 spectra on file cards of key-sort type. These catalogs are being expanded continually.

Some Spectroscopic Techniques. A practicing spectroscopist spends a good deal of his time at the business end of the spectrograph, that is, the sample holder. Preparation and handling of the sample is far from trivial when spectra are being used for qualitative or quantitative analysis. Sampling of gases is straightforward enough, but is little used today with the widespread use of mass spectrographs and gas chromatographs. Sampling of liquids and solids is usually done in absorption cells consisting basically of two plates of NaCl or KBr placed in front of the spectrometer slit. A spacer made of a foil or film about .001 inch thick is used to define the thickness of the sample layer.

Most of the liquids have such a strong absorption that they must be used either in very thin layers or must be highly diluted. The

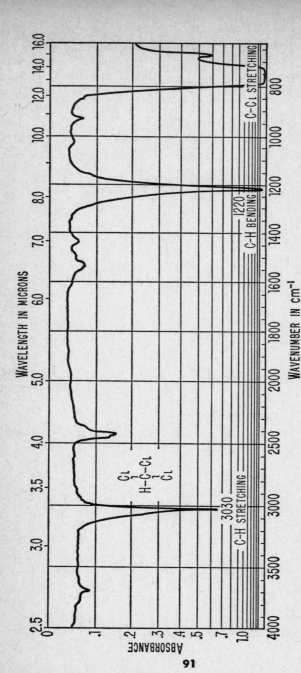

FIG. 5-6 Infrared spectrum of chloroform (CHCl₃) in liquid state. The absorption band at 3030 cm⁻¹ results from the C-H stretching vibration; the band at 1220 cm⁻¹, from the C-H bending vibration. The C-Cl vibrations at 668 and 760 cm⁻¹ are recorded very broadly because of their strong absorption. (Courtesy Dr. M. Manning, Infrared Laboratory, Arthur D. Little, Inc.)

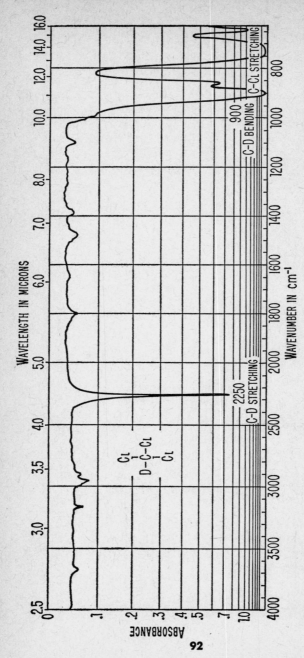

FIG. 5-7 Infrared spectrum of heavy-hydrogen substituted chloroform (CDCl₃) in liquid state. The C-D vibrations occur at lower frequencies (wavenumbers) because of the greater mass of deuterium. Since the effective mass of the C-D group (C = 12, D = 2, H = 1) is $2 \times [(12 + 1)/(12 + 2)] = 1.857$ times greater than that of the C-H group, its vibrations are $\sqrt{1.857} = 1.36$ times slower (Eq. 5-1). This is very nearly borne out by the experimental data shown above. (Courtesy Dr. M. Manning, Infrared Laboratory, Arthur D. Little, Inc.)

difficulty with the solution method is that all solvents have absorption spectra of their own. Water is particularly difficult in this respect since its fundamental OH stretching band makes it completely opaque in the 3000 to 3700 cm^{-1} region, even in the thinnest layers; it also has strong and broad bands around 2100, 1600, and 800 cm^{-1}. It does have a moderately transparent region between about 1000 and 1500 cm^{-1}, and it has a limited use there. It cannot be used with NaCl windows, which are water soluble, but one can use AgCl or BaF$_2$ windows. For organic compounds suitable solvents are CCl$_4$ or CS$_2$, the first of which is completely transparent to 1650 cm^{-1} with the exception of a weak band at 2300 cm^{-1}. Other solvents may be used when the materials are not soluble in either CCl$_4$ or CS$_2$, but their transmission is generally very limited.

Solvents are used in *quantitative analysis* when the *amount* of a given compound in a mixture is to be determined. The method is based on *Beer's law*, which may be written, following Eq. 4-2, as

$$\ln (I/I_0) = -\alpha l\gamma, \tag{5-10}$$

where γ is the concentration of the substance in unit volume and l is the thickness of the cell. It is customary here to use decimal logarithms and transmittance $T = I/I_0$. Writing $a = \alpha/\ln 10$, we obtain

$$\log_{10} (1/T) = al\gamma; \tag{5-11}$$

$\log_{10} (1/T)$ is called *absorbance*, and many spectrometers are equipped to record it rather than I or T. Equation 5-11 is then reduced to a form convenient for practical use:

$$A = al\gamma. \tag{5-12}$$

To determine the unknown concentration γ_x of a compound x in a given sample, we determine its absorbance A_x at a selected characteristic absorption band in a cell of thickness l_x. Then we prepare a solution of the compound x of a known concentration γ_s in the same solvent and determine its absorbance A_s in a cell of thickness l_s. Since the absorption coefficient a is the same in both cases, we obtain, using Eq. 5-12,

$$\gamma_x = \gamma_s \frac{A_x}{A_s} \frac{l_s}{l_x}.$$

For *qualitative analysis* it is not necessary to know the sample thickness, as long as it is adequate for obtaining well-defined and not too strong (flat-bottomed) bands. It is then often sufficient to place a drop of liquid between two NaCl plates or let a solution of the sample evaporate on one of the plates. Solid materials usually have absorption too strong to allow direct transmission; in powders loss of transmittance is aggravated by scattering of radiation. Because scattering is proportional to the difference in refractive indices, some improvement is gained by putting the finely ground solid in a liquid medium of matching index of refraction. The medium also serves as diluent. A purified hydrocarbon oil (nujol) or a fluorocarbon polymer oil (fluorolube) is often used; both of them have, of course, their own absorption bands. To prepare such an *oil-mull* sample one grinds a few milligrams of the powder in a drop of oil until a fine paste is obtained. This is then spread in a thin layer between the NaCl plates.

Another technique for preparing dilute solid samples is the KBr pellet method originated by Sister Miriam M. Stimson. The sample is ground with powdered KBr and then compacted in an evacuated die under approximately 10,000 psi pressure in a laboratory hydraulic press. The thin disc thus formed is found to be sufficiently transparent, and it shows noticeable scattering only at wavelengths shorter than about 4μ. Since KBr is hygroscopic and it is almost impossible to eliminate atmospheric water, the OH band around 3300 cm^{-1} is always found in the samples prepared by this method. Materials other than KBr may be used; powdered polyethylene sometimes offers advantages.

Still another way of obtaining spectra of strongly absorbing solids has recently been devised by J. Fahrenfort and introduced under the name of attenuated total reflection (ATR) method. In this method a small prism or a semicylinder of a highly refractive material (AgCl or KRS-5) is inserted in the optical path (Fig. 5-8) and the angle of incidence arranged so that total reflection occurs on the back face of the prism when there is no sample there. Now, if the sample is placed in optical contact with the face of the prism, total reflection is partially destroyed at those wavelengths at which the index of sample matches that of the prism. The degree to which the reflection is attenuated is determined by the absorption coefficient of the solid. As the wavelength is varied, reflection is reduced at every absorption band, and thus one obtains a spectrum similar to a conventional absorption spectrum. Because of the peculiarities of the reflection process the two spectra may not be identical as far as the intensity and precise wavelength of the bands is concerned.

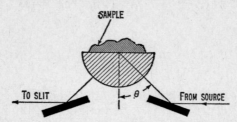

FIG. 5-8 Attachment for obtaining spectra of solids by attenuated total reflection.

It is, of course, possible to use front-face reflection directly to obtain infrared spectra of solids. This method has been widely used with single crystals and other solids when studying lattice vibrations. The reflection bands are often altered beyond recognition from the absorption bands, and elaborate computation or graphical analysis is required to obtain the true vibration frequencies. The direct reflection method is too insensitive to weak absorptions to be of value in practical spectroscopy.

REFERENCES

F. O. Rice and E. Teller, *The Structure of Matter* (John Wiley & Sons, New York, 1949).

G. Herzberg, *Infrared and Raman Spectra of Polyatomic Molecules* (D. Van Nostrand Company, Princeton, N.J., 1945).

G. Herzberg, *Spectra of Diatomic Molecules* (D. Van Nostrand Company, Princeton, N.J., 1950).

E. B. Wilson, Jr., J. C. Decius, and P. C. Cross, *Molecular Vibrations* (McGraw-Hill Book Company, New York, 1955).

W. J. Potts, Jr., *Chemical Infrared Spectroscopy*, Vol. I, *Techniques* (Vol. II, *Spectral Interpretation*, in preparation) (John Wiley & Sons, New York, 1963).

6 Some Applications of Infrared Radiation

RADIATION HEAT TRANSFER

When two bodies at different temperatures are physically separated but within "view" of each other, they exchange heat by radiation. The most grandiose example of this phenomenon is the transfer of radiant energy from the sun across the vast expanse of near-perfect vacuum to the earth. On a much more mundane scale we encounter problems in radiant heat transfer in designing heaters and boilers, vacuum-insulated containers for liquefied gases, or satellites and space ships.

Consider two parallel plates of rough, opaque material of emissivity ϵ at temperatures T_1 and T_2 and of such large extension that radiation loss at the edges is negligible. Using Eqs. 1-4 and 1-10, we see that the amount of radiant power transferred per unit area of surface is

$$W = \epsilon\sigma(T_1{}^4 - T_2{}^4), \tag{6-1}$$

or

$$W = \epsilon\sigma(T_1 - T_2)(T_1 + T_2)(T_1{}^2 + T_2{}^2),$$

which, for temperature differences $\Delta T = T_1 - T_2$ small compared with the average temperature $\frac{1}{2}(T_1 + T_2)$, may be written as

$$W = 4\epsilon\sigma T^3 \, \Delta T. \tag{6-2}$$

The heat transfer is thus proportional to the temperature difference, just as in conduction of heat in a solid material. The term $4\epsilon\sigma T^3$ corresponds here to what in solid conduction is called thermal conductivity. It is important to note, though, that while the thermal conductivity in solids does not vary substantially with temperature, the radiation thermal conductivity increases rapidly—viz., with the cube of temperature.

If the two parallel plates have unequal emissivities ϵ_1, ϵ_2, the ϵ in Eqs. 6-1 and 6-2 has to be replaced by

$$\epsilon' = \frac{1}{\epsilon_1^{-1} + \epsilon_2^{-1} - 1}. \tag{6-3}$$

Equation 6-1 may be generalized for two surfaces that enclose each other (e.g., a sphere in a hollow sphere or a cylinder inside a cylinder). The radiant power transferred from an inner body of surface area A_1 to an outer shell of surface area A_2 is then

$$W = \frac{\epsilon_1 \sigma A_1 (T_1^4 - T_2^4)}{1 + \epsilon_1 (\epsilon_2^{-1} - 1) A_1/A_2}. \tag{6-4}$$

This formula was derived by C. Christiansen (in 1883) from Kirchhoff's and Stefan-Boltzman's laws under assumption of diffusely emitting surfaces. When the surfaces emit specularly, the factor A_1/A_2 is to be omitted. For concentric spheres $A_1/A_2 = r_1^2/r_2^2$, and for coaxial cylinders $(l \gg r_1, r_2) A_1/A_2 = r_1/r_2$.

Equation 6-4 may be used to calculate radiant heat flux across the spacing of vacuum-insulated containers (*Dewar vessels*) such as those being used for storage and transportation of liquefied gases, particularly oxygen, nitrogen, hydrogen, and helium. In order to minimize the heat flux, and thus the rate of boil-off of the stored liquid gas, we must minimize the emissivity ϵ_1. The infrared emissivity of metals can be calculated from Eqs. 1-11 and 4-13, and we have seen that for silver at $\lambda = 10\mu$ it comes out to about $\epsilon \approx 0.01$; this agrees quite well with observed values.

It is often impractical to silverplate or goldplate the inner container of a large vacuum storage tank. Then it may be of advantage to use a reflecting shield of, say, aluminum foil, in the vacuum space between the warm and cold walls. Suppose, for simplicity, that the walls and the shield all have the same emissivity ϵ. Then a shield "floating" between the walls will assume some intermediate temperature T_i determined by the heat received and reradiated according to Eq. (6-1):

$$\epsilon \sigma (T_1^4 - T_i^4) = \epsilon \sigma (T_i^4 - T_2^4);$$

hence

$$T_i^4 = \tfrac{1}{2}(T_1^4 + T_2^4), \tag{6-5}$$

and the net radiant power transferred between the walls will be

$$W' = \tfrac{1}{2}\epsilon\sigma(T_1^4 - T_2^4). \tag{6-6}$$

Thus the effect of a radiation shield is to cut the heat transfer by a factor of 2. It may be shown that when n shields are placed between the walls the heat transfer will be reduced by a factor $(n + 1)$. Very effective thermal insulation based on this principle is obtained by placing a great number of loose layers of aluminized plastic film in the vacuum space of the Dewar vessel. An alternative way of reducing the radiative heat transfer between the walls is to fill the vacuum space with numerous microscopic barriers opaque to the infrared, either in the form of a loose, fluffy powder (expanded *pearlite*) or as a plastic foam of *polyurethane* or *polystyrene* (*styrofoam*).

When radiant energy is exchanged between two bodies which do not closely face each other and are not mutually enclosing, the energy transfer is determined by the geometrical configuration. Consider two elements dA_1, dA_2 of diffusely radiating surfaces A_1, A_2 oriented so that their normals are inclined at angles ϕ_1 and ϕ_2 to the radius vector r (Fig. 6-1). The solid angle under which dA_2 is seen from point 1 is $d\omega_2 = dA_2 \cos \phi_2/\pi r^2$. The radiant power emitted by the element dA_1 and intercepted by the element dA_2 is

$$dW_1 = \epsilon_1\sigma T_1^4 \cos \phi_1 \, dA_1 \cdot d\omega_2.$$

For the entire surface A_2 we obtain, substituting for $d\omega_2$:

$$W_1 = \epsilon_1\sigma T_1^4 \, dA_1 \int_{A_2} \cos \phi_1 \cos \phi_2 \, dA_2/\pi r^2.$$

The integral,

$$F_{12} = \int_{A_2} \cos \phi_1 \cos \phi_2 \, dA_2/\pi r^2, \tag{6-7}$$

is called the *view-factor* (or geometrical factor) of the surface A_2 from the surface A_1. In simple configurations this integral can be evaluated explicitly. In general, however, this may not be possible, and its value must be determined by numerical computation or model experiment.

Now if the surface A_2 has emissivity ϵ_2 and radiates at temperature T_2 toward the surface A_1, the net radiant power exchanged will be

$$W = \epsilon_1\epsilon_2\sigma(T_1^4 - T_2^4) \int_{A_1} F_{12} \, dA_1,$$

or, if F_{12} is constant over the surface A_1,

$$W = \epsilon_1\epsilon_2\sigma F_{12}A_1(T_1^4 - T_2^4). \tag{6-8}$$

This is the generalized form of Eq. 6-1.

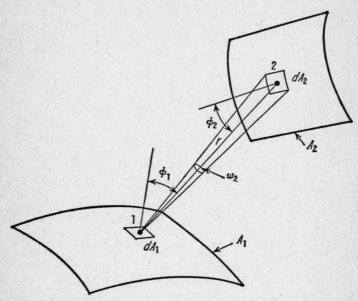

FIG. 6-1 Geometry of two bodies exchanging energy by radiative heat transfer.

An interesting example of the application of laws of radiation is the problem of control of temperature of a satellite. A passive satellite, containing no internal sources of heat, receives radiation from both the sun and the earth and re-radiates it in the space. Let us consider the sunny-side part of the orbit and assume that the heat capacity of the satellite is small enough to allow thermal equilibrium to be reached during the corresponding time interval. The balance between radiation received and emitted will determine the equilibrium temperature according to the equation:

$$W_s\alpha + W_a\alpha + W_i\alpha_i = A\sigma\epsilon T^4, \qquad (6\text{-}9)$$

where A is the radiating surface area of the satellite. Here W_s denotes the total radiant power received by the satellite from the sun, W_a is the radiant power received from solar radiation reflected by the earth (the albedo radiation), W_i is the radiant power received from earth's thermal emission, α is the absorption coefficient of the satellite surface material integrated over the solar spectral range (0.6μ peak blackbody emission curve), α_i is the absorption coefficient of the surface material in the infrared spectral range corresponding to the earth's blackbody temperature of 300°K (peak at about 10μ), ϵ is the emissivity of the surface material (in the same spectral range because the average temperature of the satellite is also about 300°K). Consequently, according to Kirchhoff's law, $\alpha_i = \epsilon$. Thus we may write

$$(W_s + W_a)\frac{\alpha}{\epsilon} + W_i = A\sigma T^4,$$

and we see that the temperature will be determined by the ratio α/ϵ.

Polished aluminum has α in the solar range about 0.3 and ϵ in the infrared range about 0.05; thus $\alpha/\epsilon = 6$. Sandblasted aluminum has $\alpha = 0.5$, $\epsilon = 0.33$, and $\alpha/\epsilon = 1.5$. White paint has typically $\alpha = 0.15$, $\epsilon = 0.9$, and $\alpha/\epsilon = 0.17$. Let us estimate the temperature of a spherical satellite in a circular orbit around the earth. If we take for the value of the *solar constant* $S = .033$ cal cm^{-2} sec^{-1} and $W_s = \frac{1}{4}AS$, the projected area of the sphere being one-fourth of its surface area, then $W_a = 0.36W_s$, assuming the value 0.36 for earth's albedo. Ignoring the term W_i for the time being, we obtain $T^4 = \frac{1}{4}(.033 + .012)(\alpha/\epsilon\sigma)$. Taking for the Stefan-Boltzmann constant $\sigma = 1.35 \times 10^{-12}$ cal cm^{-2} deg^{-4} sec^{-1} and for $\alpha/\epsilon = 1$, we obtain $T = 330$°K or 57°C. If the satellite were made of polished aluminum ($\alpha/\epsilon = 6$), it would become quite hot (500°K). If it were painted white ($\alpha/\epsilon = 0.17$), it would be very cool (210°K). Thus it is possible to control its temperature by judicious choice of the surface material. In practice the calculation is complicated by factors such as nonspherical shape, noncircular orbit, the effect of earth's radiation, and the periodic obscuration of the solar flux as the satellite passes through earth's shadow.

INFRARED RADIOMETERS

There are many occasions when it is necessary to measure temperature in places which are physically inaccessible. Think of the inside of a large open hearth furnace, or the surface of a distant planet. Under such circumstances *radiation pyrometers* can solve the problem. The well-known optical pyrometers are limited to the temperature range corresponding to visible incandescence, which is in practice above 700°C. When the eye is replaced by an infrared detector, much lower temperatures can be measured.

First applications of infrared radiometry seem to have been made by astronomers. In 1869 Lord Rosse with his great reflecting telescope of 6-ft diameter detected the thermal effect of radiation of the moon, and in 1881 Langley took his bolometer to the peak of Mt. Whitney in Sierra Nevada (14 495 ft) to determine the amount of solar radiation received by the earth. Later (1884 to 1887) Langley and F. W. Very discovered the long-wavelength component of lunar radiation and identified it as the thermal radiation of the moon proper, as distinguished from the reflected solar radiation. They also noted the surprisingly rapid cooling of the lunar surface during the eclipse. Astronomical radiometry was later (around 1930) perfected by E. Pettit and S. B. Nicholson at the Mt. Wilson observatory, who determined the temperature of the moon (134°C at subsolar point of the full moon) and also that of the planets Mercury and Mars. The temperature of Venus was determined by Coblentz and Lampland to be approximately 50°C; it appears now that it is actually much higher, perhaps over 200°C. (This is indicated by the data from a microwave radiometer carried by the Mariner-2 space probe, which approached Venus to within 22,000 miles on December 14, 1962.)

How does the infrared radiometer work? The optical system of a radiometer usually takes the form that was shown in Fig. 4-5. The mirror system is pointed so that the image of the object to be measured is formed on the detector. The radiant emittance of the object is $W = \epsilon\sigma T^4$, and the irradiance of its image is, according to Eq. 4-16,

$$W_i = \epsilon\sigma T^4 \rho D^2 / 4f^2.$$

The power absorbed by the detector generates a signal voltage, which, according to Eq. 3-5, is $V = r_0 W_i A$, r_0 being the responsivity of the detector and A its area. From the measured signal voltage we can then calculate the temperature,

$$T^4 = CV/\epsilon, \tag{6-10}$$

where $C = 4f^2/\sigma\rho D^2 r_0 A$ is a constant containing only the parameters of the instrument and the Stefan-Boltzmann constant σ. The instrument constant C is determined by pointing the radiometer at a reference blackbody of known temperature T_b and noting the corresponding detector voltage V_b. Since $\epsilon_b = 1$, we have $T_b{}^4 = CV_b$, and Eq. 6-10 may be written as

$$T = T_b(V/\epsilon V_b)^{1/4}. \tag{6-11}$$

This formula suggests a mode of operation which has become a standard feature of commercial infrared radiometers. According to Fig. 6-2 the radiation received from the object is periodically interrupted by a chopper, which throws alternately on the detector the image of the object and that of a reference blackbody. The ac voltage from the detector is amplified and converted by a synchronous rectifier in a dc voltage proportional to the difference between the two signals. The temperature of the blackbody can be adjusted until the output signal is zero. Then the effective temperature of the object is equal to the temperature of the blackbody as measured by the thermocouple attached to it. In this way the radiometer is being continually calibrated against the standard blackbody and thus becomes independent of possible changes in the parameters of the detector and the electronics.

According to Eq. 6-11 the reading of the radiometer will give the true temperature of the object only if its emissivity $\epsilon = 1$. If it is not, and the value is known, we can convert the observed effective temperature to the true temperature by dividing it by $\epsilon^{1/4}$. The fact that the emissivity of the object must be known is a serious difficulty common to all radiation pyrometers. Fortunately, in practical measurements emissivity of many materials is near unity, and so the correction is not large; sometimes it is possible to provide in the body a small cavity that serves as a blackbody.

It is possible to determine the true temperature of the object even if its emissivity is unknown, provided we measure its spectral emittance rather than its total radiant emittance and make measurements at two different wavelengths. A brief examination of Fig. 1-3

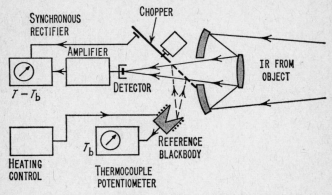

FIG. 6-2   Schematic diagram of an infrared radiometer.

shows that the ratio of emittance measured at two wavelengths can be fitted only to one isotherm of a particular temperature. This method is being used in the so-called "two-color" pyrometers. The two wavelength bands are selected by means of infrared filters, and the receiver is alternately illuminated by the two beams.

Filtering serves another important purpose even in the simple radiometers, namely, elimination of the ambient radiation. Solar radiation reflected from objects may greatly exceed their own thermal radiation which we try to measure. As long as their temperature is low compared with that of the sun, their emission is limited to the long-wavelength infrared region, while that of the sun is concentrated in the visible and very near infrared. A germanium filter with short-wavelength cutoff at about 1.8μ provides very effective separation of the two regions. Interference filters covering other wavelength regions are also available in a wide choice.

ATMOSPHERIC ABSORPTION

Radiometers are often used for detection of weak and distant sources over a great expanse of atmosphere. Atmosphere is, of course, far from being a pure substance; it is a mixture of nitrogen, oxygen, and the rare gases. It contains variable amounts of water (in gaseous,

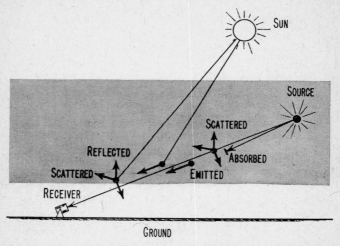

FIG. 6-3   Effect of atmosphere on propagation of infrared radiation.

liquid, or solid form), carbon dioxide, suspended particles generally classified as haze or smog, dust, etc. Radiation passing through such a turbid medium is partly absorbed and partly scattered. Solar radiation illuminating this medium is being scattered, and some of it reaches the radiometer together with the thermally emitted atmospheric radiation. Thus the radiation from the source is attenuated, and the unwanted "background" radiation is superimposed on it. This situation may be shown schematically, as in Fig. 6-3. Clearly, knowledge of these processes is of great importance both to astrophysicists and to the designers of missile detectors and trackers.

A typical atmospheric transmission curve is shown in Fig. 6-4. There are six regions in which the transmission is almost completely blocked by the H_2O and CO_2 bands, and eight "windows" in which the absorption is relatively slight. The choice of the particular window to be used in the system is determined by the temperature of the source (which determines λ_{max} of its emission curve) and by the spectral sensitivity of the detector. The two windows extending from 2.9 to 4.3μ and from 7.5 to 14μ are particularly useful. The actual transmittance in any of the windows depends principally on

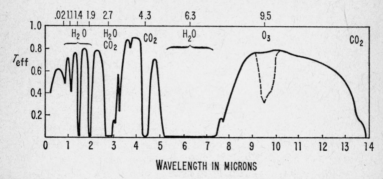

FIG. 6-4 Spectral transmittance of 2000 yards of sea-level atmosphere at low humidity and low haziness.

the amount of water in the optical path. At sea level the transmittance of a 10-nautical-mile path in clear atmosphere (48 percent relative humidity at 40°F) is about 0.50 at the midpoint of either of the two windows referred to above.

For any given concentration of water vapor the dependence of transmittance on path length x obeys very nearly the exponential law (Eq. 4-2):

$$T_a = e^{-\alpha x}.$$

The attenuation resulting from scattering by particles suspended in the atmosphere may be similarly expressed by an exponential law:

$$T_s = e^{-\beta x},$$

in which the exponent β is a function of wavelength, concentration of particles and their diameter (a), refractive index, and absorption coefficient. As far as the wavelength dependence is concerned we can distinguish three cases:

$a \ll \lambda$ (Rayleigh scattering), $\beta \propto \lambda^{-4}$;

$a \approx \lambda$ (Mie scattering), β a complex function of λ;

$a \gg \lambda$ (Nonselective scattering), β independent of λ.

Rayleigh scattering is characterized by the inverse-fourth-power dependence on wavelength. For a given particle size transmittance is much greater for longer wavelengths than for the short ones. (This explains the heavenly beauty of blue skies and the splendor of red sunsets.) *Mie scattering* varies greatly with wavelength as the wavelength becomes comparable with particle size. G. Mie derived (in 1908) the scattering coefficient of spherical particles from electromagnetic theory in the form of series expansion of Bessel functions which converge very slowly and thus are difficult to evaluate. Numerical tables of Mie functions have been computed covering a wide range of parameters. For long wavelengths $(a \gg \lambda)$ Mie scattering goes over into nonselective scattering, in which case the exponent β turns out to be nearly independent of wavelength. This is practically the most important case because water droplets in clouds and fog have sizes between 5 and 100μ and thus are a good deal bigger than the waves in the near infrared. The fact that β is independent of λ means that scattering in fog is just as bad in the infrared as it is in the visible. When attenuation is operative both by absorption and by scattering, the effective transmittance may be expressed by the product

$$T_{\text{eff}} = T_a \cdot T_s = e^{-(\alpha+\beta)x}.$$

In haze or fog, attenuation by scattering is the dominant factor. For instance, under hazy conditions characterized by a 2.5-nautical-mile visibility (in the visible red, $\lambda = 0.6\mu$), the scattering attenuation over a 10-nautical-mile path is $T_s = 0.002$. For the absorptive transmittance over the same distance we had in the preceding example $T_a = 0.50$. Thus the effective transmittance is $T_{\text{eff}} = 0.002 \times 0.5 = 0.001$. For slant paths and vertical paths the transmission becomes better, and the conditions improve rapidly with altitude as the humidity and haziness of the atmosphere disappear.

INFRARED VIEWING AND IMAGING

There is no doubt that the great advances in infrared technology during the past decade have been stimulated by the military potential of the infrared. During World War II, German, British, and U.S. military organizations supported research which led to the development of new detectors, optical materials, and detection systems. Targets of military importance, such as battleships, aircraft, and missiles, generate large amounts of heat and thus are detectable by infrared radiometry. Infrared detection systems can perform many tasks for which radar systems are used, but, owing to the much shorter wavelength, they can do it with better angular resolution and with mirrors of smaller size. The other advantage results from the fact that infrared detection systems are passive and thus emit no radiation that would reveal their operation and emplacement. The disadvantage of infrared as compared with microwaves is that propagation is strongly affected by atmospheric conditions and becomes impossible in thick fog and rain. This disadvantage is minimized in air-to-air missions. Among the most effective applications of infrared weapons systems of this type were the target-seeking and homing missiles of the Sidewinder and Falcon type. More elaborate infrared scanning detectors have been developed as fire-control sights for interceptor fighter planes, and still more sensitive scanning devices have been considered for use in early warning systems against ballistic missiles.

The first military use of an infrared viewing system was demonstrated at Fort Belvoir, Virginia, in 1942. It was a simple *image converter* used to drive a truck, equipped with infrared filters over headlights, along a road during blackout. From this were developed successively infrared binoculars, weapon sights, periscopes, and telescopes. A schematic diagram of the image converter tube can be seen in Fig. 6-5. The infrared image is focused on the transparent photocathode of the Ag-O-Cs type. The emitted electrons are accelerated across the evacuated space by a potential difference of about 15 kv toward the fluorescent screen, where they form a visible image. The electrodes are shaped so as to act as an electron lens, the focal length of which is adjusted so that a sharp electron image is formed on the screen. As seen from Fig. 3-9, the maximum sensitivity of the photocathode is at about 0.85μ, but a useful output may be obtained even at 1μ.

When the image converter tubes were declassified and became commercially available, they found numerous applications. In medical research they have been used in the ophthalmoscope and pupilometer, for studying the eye without interfering with its dark accommodation and for examination of the eye affected by keratitis,

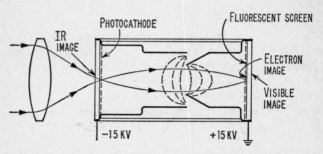

FIG. 6-5   Diagram of the infrared image converter tube.

which causes opacity of the cornea. They have also been used for studying the habits of animals in darkness. In industrial applications infrared image converters have been used, for example, for inspection of photographic film during processing.

Another infrared converter tube has been developed on the principle of the *vidicon pickup tube* currently used in television cameras. By replacing the photocathode with a photoconductive lead sulfide film, it is possible to scan the distribution of charges over its surface by an electron beam and then convert the resulting signals into a visible picture on the screen of a television receiver. The modified lead-sulfide infrared vidicons have useful sensitivity up to about 2μ wavelength.

Infrared viewing at longer wavelengths such as required for observation of objects in their self-emitted radiation can be obtained indirectly by means of a scanning radiometer. A schematic diagram of an instrument of this type (the *thermograph*) developed by R. W. Astheimer and E. M. Wormser at the Barnes Engineering Co. is shown in Fig. 6-6. The radiation from the object is imaged on the thermistor detector via a 45° mirror which is mechanically oscillated and tilted so that it scans a 10° × 20° field of view in 13 minutes. The signal from the detector is amplified and fed into the glow

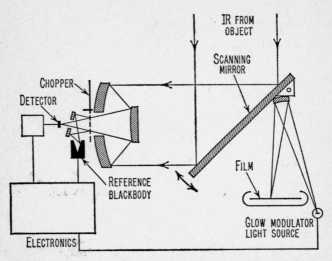

FIG. 6-6 Schematic diagram of the scanning thermographic camera.

modulator tube, which emits visible light. This light is projected on a photographic film by means of a lens and a small mirror attached to the back side of the scanning mirror. Thus, as the thermal image is being scanned, a visible image is recorded line by line on the film. The hot spots of the object appear white on the thermogram, and the cool ones remain dark. The steps of gray between the extremes can be calibrated by means of a built-in blackbody source of variable temperature. Sensitivity of the thermograph can be varied; at its maximum, it is sufficient to produce a black-to-white response for less than 1°F temperature difference.

This instrument has been used in various industrial applications, such as in distribution of heat in electronic circuit boards, nonde-structive testing of structural elements (e.g., honeycomb structures) by heat flow, examination of temperature distribution over jet and rocket engines under static test, etc. Examples of rendition of the temperature differences over the surface of a human body are shown in Plate I. The thermographic technique was proposed as a diag-nostic tool in medical research on circulatory diseases.

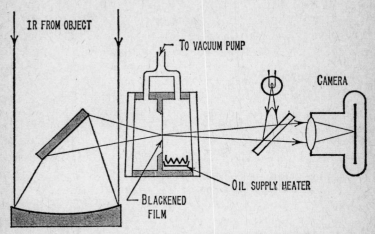

FIG. 6-7 **Schematic arrangement of the infrared evaporograph.**

Another instrument that has been used for thermal imaging is the *evaporograph* developed at the Baird-Atomic Co. Its principle goes back to John W. Herschel; in the 1930s it was greatly improved by M. Czerny and successfully used in infrared spectroscopy. The instrument is sketched in Fig. 6-7. The infrared image is formed on a thin, blackened membrane stretched across a partition in an evacuated cell. That part of the cell which is away from the ir-radiated side contains a small amount of a hydrocarbon oil and a heater which is adjusted so as to saturate the atmosphere with oil vapor at about 0.01 torr pressure. When the membrane is not irradiated, the oil film condensing on it and re-evaporating from it has an equilibrium thickness of about 0.5μ and thus becomes visible in reflected light by a uniform interference color. The infrared image projected on the membrane causes the oil film to evaporate more rapidly from the warmer areas and more slowly from the colder ones. The minute changes of the oil film thickness resulting from these temperature variations become visible as changes in the interference colors and can be photographed. Depending on the temperature of the object, the time required to develop the evaporogram may vary from a fraction of a second to a few seconds. Objects at temperatures only slightly above the ambient (e.g., human bodies) can be readily imaged by this method.

   Infrared Photography.   The use of photography in the infrared was started by another observation made by John W. Herschel, namely, that the darkening of print-out paper by visible light may be partly bleached out by exposure to infrared radiation. In studying this effect Abney (1880) developed a method for preparing special collodion emulsions which were directly sensitive to the infrared to about 1.3μ wavelength. His technique was difficult to reproduce, and so it did not find much use. Infrared photography as we know it today is based on the use of sensitizing dyes.

   Most of the dyes used for extending the sensitivity of the silver bromide emulsion (which normally lies in the blue part of the spectrum) into the infrared are derivatives of the organic base *quinoline*. The simplest compound of this type is the blue dye *cyanine* (1:1′ diethylcyanine iodide), which has the formula

The two quinoline bases are linked by one CH group; cyanine induces sensitivity with a maximum at about 0.61μ (orange). *Dicyanine* and *kryptocyanine*, with a bridge containing three CH groups, give sensitivity with a peak at 0.71μ (red) and make the emulsion sensitive up to about 1μ. *Dicarbocyanine* has five CH groups and produces peak sensitivity at 0.75μ; *tetracarbocyanine*, with eight CH groups, peaks at 0.94μ, and *pentacarbocyanine* (10 CH groups) peaks at 1.05μ. When transmission spectra of these compounds are examined, it is found that the strongest absorption bands nearly coincide with the peaks of sensitivity. The dye somehow transfers the energy which it absorbs to the crystals of silver bromide in a manner which cannot occur in the absence of the dye. The greater the size of the molecule of the dye, the longer the wavelength it absorbs and the farther in the infrared it sensitizes. The commercially available infrared-sensitive films come in various types, depending on the long-wavelength limit. The longest wavelength practically attained is about 1.35μ.

Even though this range includes only the very near infrared, the use of photographic techniques offers numerous advantages. The most important use of infrared photography is in long-distance photography (aerial reconnaissance and topographic surveys) for its ability to penetrate ground haze. Infrared, however, does not penetrate fog and mist. Landscape and ground photographs in the infrared give a very unusual rendering of colors ("moonlight effect") which must be allowed for in evaluating the surveys. The fact that the leaves of deciduous trees appear bright on infrared positives was first noted by R. W. Wood in his pioneering experiments (1910). This is usually explained by pointing out that chlorophyl is transparent to the infrared and so the internal tissues of the leaves are free to reflect the radiation. However, it has also been observed that leaves emit strong fluorescent radiation in the near infrared when illuminated by white light. An example of landscape photography in the infrared is shown in Plates II and III.

Infrared photography has its established place in astronomy and astrophysics. The first evidence for the presence of CO_2 in the atmosphere of Venus was obtained from infrared photographs of the spectra of the solar radiation reflected by the planet (W. S. Adams and T. Dunham, 1932), and the method was later applied to other planets.

In addition to medical and industrial applications similar to those discussed above, infrared photography gained notoriety in detective work of various sorts. It has been used in examining art works suspected of forgery or alteration, in deciphering old manuscripts made illegible by inquisitors' expurgations, and in restoring charred

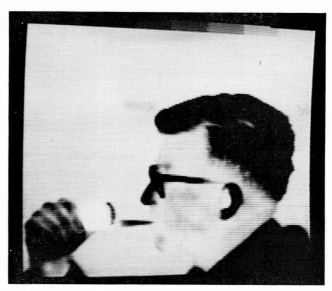

PLATE I—Thermogram (above) taken with a scanning infrared camera (Fig. 6-6). The warmer areas appear bright and the cooler ones appear dark, the entire gray scale covering a temperature difference of only a few degrees centigrade. Thermograms (below) showing abnormal and normal blood flow. (A) Inflammation resulting from a bruised elbow; (B) restricted circulation caused by a tight bracelet; (C) normal blood flow after removal of the bracelet. *(Courtesy of the Barnes Engineering Co.)*

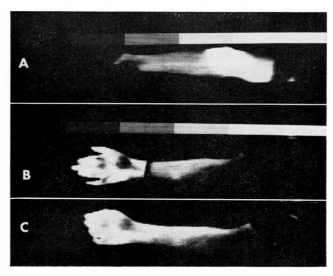

PLATE II—Aerial photograph of Rochester, N. Y., looking north, taken on panchromatic film. (*Photograph courtesy Kodak Research Laboratories*)

PLATE III—Aerial photograph of the area shown in Plate II taken on ▶ infrared-sensitive film. The water bodies appear dark because there is very little infrared radiation from the sky that they can reflect. Vegetation appears very light. The original print shows the outline of the Canadian shore of Lake Ontario which is lost in the haze in Plate II. (*Photograph courtesy Kodak Research Laboratories*)

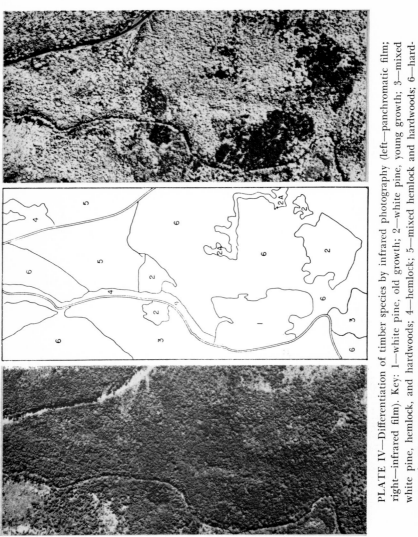

PLATE IV—Differentiation of timber species by infrared photography (left—panchromatic film; right—infrared film). Key: 1—white pine, old growth; 2—white pine, young growth; 3—mixed white pine, hemlock, and hardwoods; 4—hemlock; 5—mixed hemlock and hardwoods; 6—hardwoods. (*Courtesy Stephen H. Spurr of the Harvard Forest and Fairchild Aerial Surveys, Inc.*)

or decayed documents. In criminology it has helped to detect erasures and alterations in deeds and passports, to reveal finger-prints and bloodstains, etc. All these applications are based on the different absorption and reflection properties of dyes and pigments in the visible and infrared spectral ranges.

REFERENCES

W. H. McAdams, *Heat Transmission* (McGraw-Hill Book Company, New York, 1954).

G. Hass, L. F. Drummeter and M. Schach, "Temperature Stabilization of Highly Reflecting Spherical Satellites," J. Opt. Soc. Am. **49,** 918 (1959).

"Special Issue on Infrared Physics and Technology," Proc. I.R.E., Sept. 1959, 1420–1647.

R. Bowling Barnes, "Thermography of the Human Body," Science **140,** 870 (1963).

W. Clark, *Photography by Infrared* (John Wiley & Sons, New York, 1939).

Bibliography

L. J. Bellamy, *Infrared Spectra of Complex Molecules* (John Wiley & Sons, New York, 1954).

G. K. T. Conn and D. G. Avery, *Infrared Methods* (Academic Press, New York, 1960).

M. Davies, *Infrared Spectroscopy and Molecular Structure* (Elsevier Publishing Company, Amsterdam, 1963).

H. L. Hackforth, *Infrared Radiation* (McGraw-Hill Book Company, New York, 1960).

J. A. Jamieson, R. H. McFee, G. N. Plass, R. H. Grube, and R. G. Richards; *Infrared Physics and Engineering* (McGraw-Hill Book Company, New York, 1963).

P. W. Kruse, L. D. McGlauchlin, and R. B. McQuistan, *Elements of Infrared Technology* (John Wiley & Sons, New York, 1962).

Index